live
Happy
(...damn it)

A Journey of Acceptance and Abundance

JENNIFER CRAMER-MILLER

Jennifer Cramer-Miller

ACKNOWLEDGMENTS

Some names have been changed to protect the privacy of those individuals. Other names have been altered slightly because this book covers a long span of time…some names have become a little foggy. This is a true story, but please forgive me if I remembered something out of order. To the best of my recollections, this is how it all happened. It is also worth noting that I am not a doctor and nothing I explain in this book about my own health experiences should be in any way regarded as medical advice or expertise.

Copyright © 2013 Jennifer Cramer-Miller
Publisher: Jennifer Cramer-Miller
5500 Lincoln Drive, Ste. 180
Edina, MN 55436

ISBN 978-0-615-81311-0
Library of Congress Catalog Number Pending

Book Cover Design: Jennifer Cramer-Miller in collaboration with Karen McCall

The author is grateful for permission to reprint: Quotation from The Book of Bebb, 2001 Paperback Edition (HarperCollins Publishers) Source ISBN: 978-0-06-251769-2, Source Chapter Open Heart, Chapter 17, Page Range 251, reprinted by permission of the Frederick Buechner Literary Assets, LLC. Quotation from A Joseph Campbell Companion, Reflections on the Art of Living by Joseph Campbell, 1991, reprinted by permission of the Joseph Campbell Foundation (jcf.org). Curly Girl Design card "Even If She Weren't My Mom," artwork and words ©2008 Leigh Standley, publishing ©2008 Curly Girl Design Inc./Leigh Standley

Live Happy (...damn it)

For Dirk and Liza

Jennifer Cramer-Miller

PROLOGUE

Bubbles. Shiny, iridescent circles of various sizes coaxed a smile from my daughter as they floated in the air around us.

The photographer's tactic was effective until the bubbles glided to the ground and disappeared. Liza's fleeting smile was once again replaced with uncertainty, as her wonder vanished.

Additional tricks of distraction were utilized and our family photograph was complete. In the picture, Liza is gripping onto me tight with one hand, her Raggedy Ann doll securely clutched in the other.

She is looking at the photographer with her big chocolate brown eyes. My husband Dirk is smiling and has his arm draped around me. Liza is nestled between us as we fit together like three pieces of a small puzzle.

Liza was two in the photograph that now hangs on the buttercream colored wall in our upper level hall. When I look at this sepia toned image of my family from 1998, I feel grateful we have frozen this moment.

This picture is part of a gallery of photographs, and I feel grateful for all the pictures that hang together here. I feel grateful for the family and friends that are showcased within these frames. I feel grateful for the abundance in my life.

Jennifer Cramer-Miller

PART ONE

"If there's anything half so much fun as being alive, I'd like to know what it is."

-Frederick Buechner-

CHAPTER ONE

In 1987, I was a college senior in the Pacific Northwest. After four years of coursework, I was closing in on an undergraduate degree in business.

Before college, I contently spent eighteen years in Golden Valley, Minnesota with my mom and dad, my brother Steve, and our neurotic but lovable dog Gus.

Our traditional New England style two-story home was close to our neighborhood school, flanked by parks, and just three miles west of Minneapolis. The backdrop of my idyllic childhood was in this home on the corner of Westwood Drive and Westwood Lane.

There was not an exceptional amount of drama in our house when I was growing up. Steve and I had typical sibling rivalry when we were young, but I managed to endure his brotherly pranks without too much mental fallout.

His signature trick was to place a fake (but believe me, very realistic looking) plastic black rat in various locations around our home. I jumped and yelped when I found it in our silverware drawer, and screamed bloody murder when it was lurking under the covers of my bed.

He had other sources of fun—throwing my favorite doll Peggy overboard when we were on a family boating excursion, and the occasional catch-me-by-surprise push in a pool.

When my mom became exasperated with too much brother/sister roughhousing, she often resorted to her favorite stern command,

"Take it outside kids—take it outside!"

I grew up watching *The Brady Bunch*, and strongly identified with the tragic injustices faced by Marcia. In one episode, Greg got the bigger bedroom because he was the oldest. I identified with her dramatic plea and tried to deliver it with equal conviction. "It is not fair that I should be penalized because I was born one year later than Greg … umm…I mean… Steve."

I think that was about the time my mom put limits on my television habits.

Of course there were plenty of good things about having a brother. Steve was the only one to share the magic and excitement when Santa brought us gifts, and as the story goes, saved me from a car that was coming down the street one day by rolling me out of the way.

When my journey through childhood, middle years, and high school was over, I wanted to start fresh. I had attended three high schools in four years due to the mess of declining enrollment and public school mergers.

This high school shuffle left me lost in a sea of strangers that were my fellow students. I graduated feeling bruised from all the bouncing, and was ready to find a safe haven away from that instability.

That safe haven became a stunning campus in Tacoma, Washington. On my first visit I was enthralled by the Tudor Gothic architecture. The distinctive character of red brick and mortar, glass, stone, and stately evergreens shared space with a warm collegiate community. This place called to me instantly.

So I boldly traded familiar surroundings, distinct seasons (winter blizzards and humid summers) for the unfamiliar, temperate, and wet Washington climate. I boarded a plane to Seattle, not knowing anyone, and found myself on the west coast in Washington at the

Live Happy (...damn it)

University of Puget Sound.

CHAPTER TWO

S teve had started college the year before in upstate New York, so my departure officially launched my parents into empty-nester status.

I would not let my mom and dad take me to the airport because I was afraid to say goodbye to them in public; I was afraid I would be emotionally messy.

So, I held it together at home as I hugged them and tentatively said "See you later." My friends Rachael and Beth picked me up and whisked me to the Minneapolis/St. Paul airport.

As my flight was called and I was ready to board the plane, I turned and said sheepishly to Rae and Beth "What if no one likes me?"

"Don't worry." Rachael said with reassurance, "You're the likeable type." Armed with her encouragement I walked down the ramp and boarded the plane bound for Seattle.

I took a shuttle from the Seattle airport to travel 30 miles south to the campus at the north end of Tacoma. I was immersed in a different part of the country with fresh faces from all over the United States. Soon I had new friends from Alaska, California, Colorado, Hawaii, and Washington.

Although it was never a distinction for me before, I became the

"Minnesota girl." My west coast cohorts were amused by my Minnesota accent as I said "pop" instead of "soda," and my "yeah" had a twang.

Todd Hall became my dormitory home and my new roommate Kirsten and I shared a bunk bed and cramped quarters. Magnetically, my fellow dorm mates and I came together during our first semester. Cindy, Susan, Nick, Ron, Scott, John, Mike and I were woven into a tight knit and comfortable fabric.

Together, we divided our time between enlightening class discussions, cross campus walks in drizzling rain with books and umbrellas, way too many pizzas, and exuberant parties to decompress from the academic pressure.

Michael Jackson, Madonna, Culture Club, and Duran Duran were at the height of popular culture and permeated the radio and MTV. We favored U2, The Cure, Prince, and The Smiths. We were unaware at the time that our hair was too big, and stirrup pants and shoulder pads were to become fashion embarrassments.

Cindy was a cute blonde basketball player, and exuded the sunny disposition of a California girl. You would have never guessed by looking at her enviable athletic body that her diet consisted mainly of canned pink frosting, dehydrated potato buds, and cheddar cheese Ruffles (generously dipped in sour cream).

Like me, Susan was a wholesome Minnesota girl. Although we first met at Puget Sound, she grew up a mere fifteen miles west of my hometown of Golden Valley. Her generous smile, sparkling blue eyes, and refreshing demeanor made her an easy target for an instant friend.

After our first semester in Todd Hall, some of us felt a palpable social energy in the Greek system that existed outside our dormitory walls. We were curious about enhancing our social experiences, and considered expanding our horizons.

I called Steve in New York to get his thoughts on whether or not I should join a sorority. I was hesitant as I told him that the particular house I liked did not have a great reputation.

"Some people describe the Pi Phis as pretty, rich girls—a little stuck up." I reported.

"What?!" That is the best reputation you can get!!" he exclaimed.

Despite this "reputation," the girls we met at the Pi Phi house were amazing, so Susan, Cindy and I joined the group. Nick joined the SAE fraternity. We jumped on the social ladder and started to climb.

Nick was perfectly suited for a fraternity. He shined in a group. When he walked into a room the air changed—he injected it with an energy that fostered a good time. He grew up in Anchorage, and his self-deprecating humor was entertaining and engaging. We became good friends.

After Cindy, Susan and I moved into the Pi Phi house, I met Lisa. She was also a freshman, and we shared a Communications class.

At first she seemed reserved. Although her energy was self-contained, her beauty was striking. Her peaches-and-cream complexion was framed with the thickest mane of honey blonde hair I had ever seen. I was not sure if she was shy, or just full of herself.

I sat behind her in class and noticed she had a habit of picking her lower lip, as if the repetition helped her focus. I stood up at the end of class and said "See you later Lisa."

She looked at me with kind blue eyes and said "Thanks—you too!" Hardly a remarkable exchange—but she pumped a little extra into it and I could tell we had a friendship on the way. We found we shared unique perceptions and an affinity for silliness.

Many parties in the Greek system were incomplete without a

theme. The lively Fiesta. The classic Toga. The macabre Embalmer's Ball. At a pledge party with the ever-popular pajama theme—we donned flannel nightgowns and geared up to meet the new potential Pi Phis.

Beverages were running low, so Lisa and I were dispatched to the nearby Piggly Wiggly grocery store to re-stock. On our way we passed another sorority having a party outside on their lawn. We glanced over to see them dressed like regular people in regular clothes.

Simultaneously, we realized the absurdity of our mid-day (flannel, of course!) pajamas as we headed to the store. Words were unnecessary—we just laughed at our ridiculousness as we zipped along Union Street.

Cindy, Susan, Lisa, Nick and I all became very good friends, and over several months, my friendship with Nick progressed to romance. I thrived in this world beyond Minnesota that boasted of challenging academics, the waters of Puget Sound, lush greenery, sushi, Starbucks, and newfound companions. Together we navigated that magical space between high school and real life.

CHAPTER THREE

The four years in Tacoma flew by. We all packed up and felt excited to explore new adventures in Seattle. Lisa was not sure what career she was going to pursue, but she had a keen sense of style and loved shopping. She soon got a job selling hosiery at Nordstrom. This suited her for the time being, the discount was useful, and she had a way to pay rent.

Cindy had dreams of becoming a stockbroker and found an internship at a large investment company downtown. In addition, she secured a job at the Bon Marche department store to pay her bills, prior to making big bucks in the stock market.

With a business major and psychology minor in hand—I also set out to launch my career. Like Cindy, I too landed an internship and started working at a respected public relations firm named Cole & Weber. It was very exciting and I was delighted to be chosen.

Great experience. Insignificant income. So also like Cindy, I worked at the Bon Marche. As I generated a paycheck selling accessories and special occasion dresses, I sponged up all I could about the field of public relations.

The three of us found an apartment in the Capitol Hill area of Seattle. Although Capitol Hill was known as a tough neighborhood peppered with homeless people and crime—we were not deterred. We were overjoyed to find a place we could afford. Apartment F on

Broadway became our new home.

Apartment F was an older two-story house split into two apartments on the main level, and two apartments on the upper floor. We rented the right side of the main level—three bedrooms, a living room, and a small kitchen. The stained, gold, shag carpet was a visual companion to the stale, musty odor that permeated the space. Home sweet home.

One of the bedrooms was large with a bay window that faced Broadway. The other two were quite a bit smaller so the three of us drew straws. Lisa's luck prevailed and she took the bigger room. Cindy and I took the two smaller rooms that were farther down the hall closer to the living room and kitchen. We settled in and our new lives in the city of Seattle began.

Street parking was very limited. There was a church lot close by, but parking was prohibited there between specified hours. To enforce this restriction, a large barrel was attached with a chain to an offending car's tire after 7:00 am.

If barreled you could 1) call the company to request someone to de-barrel your car for $50.00 or 2) drive off and let the barrel smash your car. It wasn't really a choice. Many times we overslept our 7:00 a.m. deadline—awakening in a sudden panic.

"Oh no!"

"Barrel?"

"Barrel."

The morning barrel was irritating and $50.00 was a big chunk out of our measly salaries. Yet we would often park there instead of parking farther away from the apartment.

It was frightening to park farther down the road because we often heard a sinister "Good night" coming from the roadside bushes as we rushed past to get home. Strange voices drifting out of rustling bushes seemed more ominous than the dreaded barrel.

The various characters on Broadway were a sharp contrast to our college campus crowd. A wonderful man from Poland would frequently stop by our neighborhood to give away freshly baked bread (fondly known to us as the "Polish Man").

He wore a wool cap over his white hair, and modest clothes with tweed knickers. We would often see him on the sidewalk passing out bread from a big wicker basket on the front of his bike. Like kids running to the ice cream truck, we enthusiastically greeted the Polish Man. His broken English and kindness were endearing. Never selling, just sharing.

Unfortunately, not all our visitors were as charming. We had a Peeping Tom that would walk down the sidewalk that flanked our apartment at night, and stare into the living room window. Naively, we just accepted him as a feature of the apartment.

We were young. We were stupid. We noticed him, mentioned it to each other, and carried on.

"There is he again."

"I saw him last night, did you?"

"Yeah, I did too."

We regarded him as a bizarre novelty. It was not until my Minneapolis cousin Ellen came to visit me with two of her friends that we became more attentive. As we all gathered one evening in the living room, the shadow of the large man appeared in the window. Ellen's friend Tom stood up, walked to the window, and our Peeping Tom scurried away.

"What the hell?" Tom said as we all just sat there watching television.

We casually reassured him, "Don't worry, that always happens."

We were faced with open jaws and incredulous stares from Ellen,

Tom, and her friend Sue. Their looks of horror and concern clarified that this may be a safety issue. We got the clue and decided to move.

We started searching for a new apartment, but the situation boiled over before we found one. We were robbed. Lisa and I came home, Cindy shortly after—and discovered chaos.

Clothes had been stolen from our closets and it was a huge mess. Condoms were scattered all over the place. We each briefly assumed they belonged to the other, only to find they were scattered by our culprit. We got out fast.

CHAPTER FOUR

Lisa and I found a lovely apartment in the charming and safe neighborhood of Queen Anne. We rented a U-Haul truck, filled it with our stuff, and set off to our new place. I quickly declined to be the driver of the clunky truck, so Lisa reluctantly jumped in the driver seat.

As we drove up the steep hill of Queen Anne to get to apartment #303, the crudeness of the shift mechanism became apparent. As Lisa was trying to balance her release of the brake with the gas to propel us up the hill—we started to slide backward.

"Lis—you are going backward!' I screamed.

"I can't drive this truck!" Lisa barked as she struggled to find the balance between the shift's acceleration and clutch.

She leaned forward with a death grip on the plastic steering wheel, found the sweet spot, and slowly we started to inch up the hill. Fear, tension, excitement, exhaustion, and relief united into nervous giggles, then whole-hearted laughter. Dumb and Dumber…on the move.

Cindy decided to fly the friendly skies and became a Pan Am flight attendant. She discovered the world of blue and red uniforms, red lipstick, bobby pins, weigh-ins, and an unwelcome focus on her appearance. All of this coupled with fun travels and new friends.

She moved to London and lived with three other women, one

from Jamaica, one from Switzerland, and one supermodel. She entered a more glamorous world than we once had in Tacoma.

Meanwhile, Susan had moved into a rental house with her friend Laura from Minnesota. We saw each other on weekends and at parties, but less frequently due to the reduced proximity.

Nick stayed in Tacoma and lived with buddies while he completed credits for his degree. We were still dating and he came to Seattle often. We went out to dinner at restaurants on Lake Union, enjoyed cocktails on top of the Space Needle, and explored new sushi spots. We also went downtown on weekends to drink and dance with good friends—we made the most of our youthful energy.

My internship was going well. The office was chaotic and the full-time staff was swamped. A project presented itself that was not intended for an intern but everyone else was too busy. It was handed to me and I jumped.

Cole & Weber represented the Seattle based Westin hotels. A Japanese corporation bought the Westin chain, and the Seattle Westin staff was concerned about the possible implications. A report was immediately requested on the background of the new owners.

I felt pressure because my deadline was immediate. Fortified with an intense need to please management and stressful exhilaration—I rushed and raced to gather and assemble information for a complete report. (This was a much larger task prior to the ease of Internet searches. If you can believe...I actually had to make phone calls and compile research at a *library*.)

My report was approved by the top management at Cole & Weber (owned and a subsidiary of Ogilvy & Mather) and then went to the President of the Westin Hotels. My name was front and center on the report and I felt accomplished, proud, and excited for all the opportunities ahead.

I was happy with all the pieces of my life. Budding public relations career, selling accessories for a paycheck, the city of Seattle, close friends, and a fun boyfriend.

CHAPTER FIVE

November 19, 1988

This Thursday should have been just another gray day. I woke up in my typical foggy state. I was always a slow starter so Lisa knew not to expect any reasonable form of conversation until I had at least two cups of strong coffee.

This particular morning, however, my wake-up fog seemed thicker. The cobwebs were not clearing from my brain, and my eyes were quite puffy. Premenstrual puffy? Too much salt? All the usual suspects entered my mind as I slowly plowed on with my day.

"Hey Jenn, you okay?" Lisa said as she popped her head in my room in the late morning.

"Not feeling great—maybe I have a bug."

"You want to go out for a cappuccino?"

"No—I'm gonna take it easy. Thanks anyway."

"See ya—okay?"

"Sure—I'll see ya later." Lisa went out. I went back to bed.

My energy was low. I got up, drank some extra coffee, and hoped the discomfort would resolve itself. It got worse—puffy ankles were complimenting my puffy eyes. I drank more fluid trying to flush the fluid I was retaining—but it did not help. There was no flush.

I called Nick and told him I was really puffy. He suggested I drink some alcohol for its diuretic effects. "I'll take you out for cocktails tonight—booze you up—what time should I come get you?"

"No, really. I think there is something wrong…it's weird. Just come over—skip the booze."

I had frequent headaches in college, so I always had a supply of Nuprin on hand when the throbbing started. Aside from these headaches I did not have any health concerns, so my recent symptoms seemed out of the blue.

I called my parents in Minneapolis and my dad jumped into action. He tracked down a referral for a Seattle internist from his doctor in Minneapolis. I called the doctor's number and made an appointment. They accommodated me right away.

Off I went in my efficient and reliable charcoal gray Honda Civic to an office in the University District. I explained my puffy dilemma to a kind older doctor with white hair and a soft manner. He ordered some urine tests and came back with a vague but disturbing report.

"The results indicate your kidneys are damaged. You need to have a biopsy to determine the extent and cause of the damage."

"What?" I thought. "Biopsy…isn't this a cancer related word? What are you talking about? My friend Sarah is having a swanky party in just over a week, so please just fix me. What happened to something simple—something like the flu?"

My concerned Mom booked the first flight from Minneapolis to Seattle and stayed with Lisa and me for a few days. She cooked us turkey breast with vegetables and a salad. Lisa and I sat at the table with her, and had our first real meal in our Queen Anne apartment.

Our typical dinners consisted of diet pops and plastic-wrapped grocery store sushi. In contrast, this meal was spiced with the warmth and flavor that only comes from a home cooked Mom-meal.

The depth of concern in my mom's eyes was unnerving. She saw something in mine that broadcast scary medical events were ahead. Moms always know, and she knew.

I suppose we all learn sooner or later that life has a fist. Life's fist was about to knock me down.

CHAPTER SIX

My mom and I flew back to Minneapolis and the march of medical events began.

Although I thought I was going home to Minneapolis for the convenience of getting a quick "fix" with family support, my mom felt sure that whatever was brewing required more.

My dad is a well-respected custom homebuilder in the Minneapolis suburbs. The homes that fill his portfolio are impressive, and the clients who build them are equally so.

Years prior, Dr. Brown had my dad's company build an art-filled contemporary home in the hillside of an established Minneapolis area called Kenwood. He and his wife relied on my dad's expertise to build their lovely home.

We could have never guessed that our family would eventually need to rely on Dr. Brown's expertise in nephrology.

Dr. Brown was called and he scheduled a biopsy. The results came back, and he reported, "You may have a progressive kidney disease." Few words. Immense impact.

My water retention, low blood albumin level, and protein in the urine indicated I had a condition called nephrotic syndrome. There are various causes for nephrotic syndrome, and my biopsy showed I had an autoimmune disease called focal segmental glomerulosclerosis (FSGS).

Instantly, my twenties felt robbed of promise. Just a month ago I was on track with what I believed would be my glorious future. Some puffiness, a trip home, a biopsy, some powerful words—and my future seemed suddenly altered.

I felt torn from the Velcro that attached me to my life—Lisa, Cindy, Nick, Seattle, Sarah's upcoming party, all my college friends, and my soon-to-be-impressive career.

Painfully, suddenly...ripped away.

MEDICAL 101

Now that I had a diagnosis surely the doctors would know how to fix my problem, or so I thought. Not so. My first medical lesson was doctors do not have all the answers.

Instead of a quick cure I was faced with varied and confusing medical viewpoints. Five doctors had five opinions on how to treat my condition and different guesses on the likely rate of progression.

Nephrotic syndrome indicates there is inflammation in the filters of the kidney—the nephrons. A healthy kidney does not let proteins pass through the nephrons, just like a coffee filter prevents coffee grounds from getting into your coffee. My nephrons were like a coffee filter with holes.

Kidneys are little organs (approximately the size of a human fist) with a big job. They remove waste products from the blood, regulate fluid balance, sodium and potassium levels, control blood pressure, and stimulate the production of red blood cells.

Dr. Brown explained there is a child-onset nephrotic syndrome that does respond well to treatment. It was unclear at the age of 22, if I was experiencing a late child-onset case, or if my case was more advanced.

The haziness of my diagnosis mirrored the confusing intersection of time and place in my life. I was not a child, and not perfectly positioned within adulthood. I was in life stage limbo—the space between reliance and independence. I was in the process of forging my way into the post-college world, and hadn't quite put the last puzzle piece into place.

One place, however, I knew I fit, without question. I was my parents' daughter. And that is why I immediately, and instinctively called home. I knew where to turn. Like my private National Guard, I knew my mom and dad would swiftly engage for disaster response.

CHAPTER SEVEN

There was no sure fire treatment for FSGS, but some patients had responded to high doses of prednisone. The plan was to see if I had a positive response to this anti-inflammatory drug.

Prednisone is prescribed for many conditions and can have amazing results. It can also be a nasty drug in high doses; the side effects can be bizarre and disturbing.

My internist explained, "You may feel extremely hungry, gain weight, have personality changes and become manic or anxious, your muscles may atrophy so your legs and arms may become very skinny, your cheeks may puff up so you obtain a moon face, develop high blood sugar, insomnia, plus it can weaken your bones and cause cataracts."

Oh great...sign me up!

I was ready to take anything to rid my body of this proteinuria and kidney damage. If it progressed, I would need to have a kidney transplant, and I just couldn't imagine it. It sounded so severe—so movie-of-the-week, so not how I expected my life to unfold in my twenties.

Fix me!

Dr. Brown also mentioned there had been rare cases of spontaneous remission. I decided that was the route I wanted to take. I became devoted to pouring positive thoughts into that outcome. My plan was to have a spontaneous remission, and then go back to

Seattle and pick up where I left off.

Spontaneous remission, spontaneous remission, spontaneous remission, spontaneous remission, spontaneous remission, spontaneous remission, spontaneous remission, spontaneous remission.

If this was a movie of the week—this would be the part where I miraculously recovered and lived happily ever after. Unfortunately, I was not in control of the script.

Some doctors felt I had "a significant cosmetic problem" due to my kidney's failure to manage water retention. Some doctors felt I was headed for kidney failure and a kidney transplant.

Some doctors felt I should take powerful chemotherapy drugs, with the hope these medications would eliminate the inflammation and close the protein leak. Some doctors felt these medications may not work, could be very harmful, and may eliminate the possibility that I would ever have children.

I was being pumped with huge doses of prednisone, bombarded with contrasting messages, and feeling the symptoms of compromised kidneys: tired; weak; swollen; anemic; loss of appetite; high blood pressure; elevated potassium blood levels; and cloudy thoughts.

CHAPTER EIGHT

I was flooded daily with so many great cards, flowers, and letters from my college friends back in Seattle. I felt grateful and touched and I could not wait to get back to my life.

My close friend Gillian had started teaching first grade in the Seattle area, and she told her students about my situation. She asked them to make cards for her sick friend in the hospital. I received a heartwarming package of sweetly drawn crayon pictures from her class.

My favorite was a crayon drawing of a girl in a bed, looking like she was being electrocuted. Above her artwork of a girl with frantic hair and a distressed expression—the kindergartener wrote in precious handwriting *"Your* pretty."

Friends were worried, and calls and cards kept coming. I started to get scared. Depressed. I slowly started retreating into myself as this illness kept up its stubborn stance against the prednisone treatment.

All the while Lisa was waiting for me to come back to Seattle. I was sending half of the rent to her to hold my spot. Yet my quick fix was not so quick, and Lisa was anxious to have a roommate again. I just couldn't face the fact that I would not be able to go back.

"Hi Jenn—how ya doing?"

"Well—my hair is falling out and I look horrible. How is Seattle…I miss you a lot."

"Miss you too. What do your doctors say?"

"They say I need to wait to see if the prednisone works. I think it will. I just can't imagine it won't. It has to—just be patient please Lisa. I really want to come back soon."

"I know you do. Just get better okay?"

"I will."

Then we would both hang up with heaviness in our hearts and fear that getting better might not be the case.

It was a difficult moment when my mom told me to face the truth; it wasn't fair to Lisa. So with reluctance I called and told her the news—I wasn't coming back anytime soon.

Lisa was shaken. I was devastated. My denial was shattered. I wasn't going to squeak out of this ordeal. Cindy generously offered to drive my car to Minneapolis for me and we flew her back home. Lisa moved in with her high school friend Denise, and I felt wiped off the board.

I felt a profound sense of loss. Lost energy. Lost ambition. Lost innocence. Lost health. Lost promise and anticipation for the life I had just begun to set in motion.

My college pictures from six months earlier were a stark contrast to my current state. I wanted to reclaim my carefree spirit, apple cheeks, shining brown eyes and thick brunette hair; I wanted to reclaim the girl I used to be—such a short time ago.

Most of my high school friends were not in town, so I felt isolated being back in Minneapolis. They called often with prayers and warm wishes, but they were scattered throughout the country. Colorado, New Mexico, California, Oregon, and Wisconsin. It was easier to talk on the phone anyway because I was painfully self-conscious about my prednisone-altered appearance.

Racheal came into town and called to say she wanted to come over and see me. I told her I didn't look good and she would have to wait. She said that was ridiculous and came anyway.

My Seattle friends also continued to call often and I spoke obsessively about my hair falling out. After so many conversations, they did not know what to say. They felt helpless as they watched me fall overboard with no lifesavers in sight.

CHAPTER NINE

My mom was there every step of the way. She felt it was her battle to take on with me, and take it on she did. We took notes on the many theories of the many doctors. Dr. Brown was in charge.

I was hospitalized for repeated biopsies, albumin infusions, and observation at Abbott Northwestern Hospital, a teaching institution. I became the subject and some of the young interns were just too enthusiastic to learn.

A young resident bound into my hospital room one day with great excitement and inquired, "Do your legs hurt? You can get clots in your legs—it happens when you stay in bed! Tell me…do your legs hurt?"

"I hate to let you down but my legs feel okay. Tone it down a bit—how's that for a lesson in the teaching hospital," I thought to myself bitterly.

The history, the history, the history—they all came in to hear the medical history. Painstaking detailed questions were asked and answered as the young doctors took careful notes to learn about various betrayals of the body.

My first accounts were spot-on accurate—dates, feelings, changes, T's crossed and I's dotted. After I told it time and again, it began to bore me and lost some of its razor sharp precision.

I had crossed a line—I saw a clear division between healthy normal people whose worlds kept turning, and sick people like me whose wheels were spinning in place.

I heard about all the Seattle parties I was missing, the new jobs people were getting, the new boyfriends that were being acquired. Life in Seattle seemed ideal. It was the world I wanted to be in and it felt so far away.

I became embroiled in my medical care in Minneapolis. Doctor appointments, theories, medical protocols, prescription changes and procedures. Day after day, my parents helped me travel through this unknown medical land.

At one point I went to Dr. Brown's office and my legs were so swollen I could hardly move them. He said enough was enough, I did not have to be that swollen and he admitted me to Abbott hospital.

I received an albumin infusion and intravenous Lasix. Lasix is a diuretic that assists the kidneys with their fluid elimination, and the IV form of the drug is more potent than Lasix pills.

The albumin helped draw fluid out of my cells, and the Lasix enabled my kidneys to pee out the extra fluid volume that had collected in my body.

It felt miraculous. All of a sudden I was peeing! I remembered what it used to be like and I was so happy. After a few days of this treatment I left the hospital thirty pounds lighter. I may have still had my kidney disease, but I looked good again.

But the fix was only temporary and slowly the water weight returned. For every upward notch on the scale, I lost my desire to be in the world. Each additional pound of water retention felt like a visible measurement of disease.

CHAPTER TEN

Dr. Brown truly cared about me and he really wanted to make things better. Although he could not offer a cure, he offered his compassion and heart.

I was somehow attacking my own kidneys with an autoimmune disease. Why would my body betray me this way? I faded into myself. My pale complexion mirrored the loss of color in my life.

Through it all, my mom was by my side. She lightened the heavy load and kept peppering humor into the chaos. We considered my many doctor appointments as a form of recreation, and referred to each one as a "riot."

"Doctor appointment tomorrow at 2:00 Mom."

"Great! Where we going?"

"Urologist—need to scope my bladder."

"Riot!"

We went on many so-called "riots"—always battling the unpleasant nature of the outing with humor. We were just glad to be together in good spirits and made the best of it. My mom is an all-star at bringing light to a dim situation.

We laughed our way through much of the ordeal. One day in the hospital my mom tried to straighten out the complex intersection of plastic lines from multiple IV medications, and proceeded to completely tangle herself within them.

As she comically tried to free herself, she resembled a wacky

Lucille Ball in one of her zany misadventures. At times we felt we had starring roles in our own personal medical sitcom.

CHAPTER ELEVEN

My mom and I quickly learned that a hospital patient needs support. It is difficult to get everything straight and fight for your cause when you are ill, medicated, bombarded, and overwhelmed. My mom was my fierce ally and advocate, or as we called her, my "Avocado."

"I have to go to the hospital and have a procedure, can you be my Avocado?" I often asked.

"Sure, I'll get my notebook." she responded cheerfully.

I read all the books I could on miracle cures. I devoured Bernie Siegel's book *Love, Medicine, and Miracles*. Although it made me feel empowered, I also felt pressure.

Can all cancers and illnesses be due to faulty thinking? If I change my thoughts can I heal myself and turn this around? Part of me felt hopeful with the message of positive thinking, and part of me felt like a judgmental finger pointed at me and said, "Shape up your mind!"

I was looking for healing in all sorts of places. I went to a chiropractor that utilized a system called Applied Kinesiology. This technique utilizes manual muscle testing and response to evaluate body imbalances. He told me I had mercury poisoning and put me on a mess of minerals and more pills.

I sheepishly ran this list of minerals by Dr. Brown to get his "approval" (as always, I was seeking approval.) He scrunched up his face, peered at me through his professor-like spectacles and questioned, "Who told you to take these?"

I could see I was blowing his medical mind—it smacked of quackery to him.

Unconvincingly, I said "an internist?" I didn't think I would have gotten far by saying "A chiropractor/healer who pulled on my arm." Needless to say, he firmly responded with "Don't take them, they could harm you." So that was that.

I also had a session with a musicologist (recommended by the arm pulling chiropractor). I had never heard of this discipline before but I figured I had nothing to lose. He was an older man who was quite enthusiastic about the healing powers of music.

I met him in a small room (similar to a psychologist's office) as he explained his approach. He said he would ask me questions with subtle music in the background. My job was to answer with whatever came to my mind. It sounded easy—and although I was doubtful it would do anything for me, I was game.

First he blindfolded me. Then he started to ask me questions and I rambled. I don't remember much about the beginning of the session but I do remember the end. I saw myself in a field with Steve and we were very young.

As if I was a vulnerable child, I told the Musicologist that I did not like it when Steve was mean to me. He told me to tell Steve. I imagined doing so. Then he told me to hit a punching bag. I think this was my retribution for when my doll Peggy was thrown overboard. Done. Next?

I saw myself approaching a lake—it was blue and clear and I wanted to jump in. I told him that I did not think I should; I was afraid to jump in the water.

He encouraged me to jump in. I can't remember if I did or not—

but I did start to cry. This felt like another release and it seemed to unload some weight from my being.

He said water frequently represents sexuality and may reflect risk taking. I didn't know what that meant exactly, but it made me wonder if I should start jumping in some more lakes.

The session was done. Although I had been skeptical, I actually felt a sense of clarity—magically through music manipulation. Who knew?

He asked if he could give me a hug (which my Aunt Lucy disapprovingly claimed was a boundary violation). I said okay to the hug and I left.

Then I spent a solid month in the hospital.

CHAPTER TWELVE

Hospitals are mood-altering places and the hospital environment changed how I felt. My dignity evaporated with admission.

The worn and faded light blue hospital gown drained any last trace of color from my pale face. My identity became a room number. Bed 22-A. I constantly heard the nurses and doctors outside my room, "We need vitals and weight for 22-A."

The hospital surfaces were also disconcerting. The linoleum tile floor was sticky and stained with dark orange-brown Betadine solution and drops of blood. It never felt clean, especially after I saw the janitors with big floppy mops systematically dilute, swish, and spread the stickiness and body fluids around.

The shower curtain in the small bathroom created a tricky proposition. It took skill to shower in this tiny space and simultaneously dodge the plastic curtain's attempt to suction itself onto me. The challenge was greater when paired with IV tubes and surgical incisions.

I longed to be Jennifer again—happy-go-lucky in Seattle with lots of friends and vitality. Instead I felt I had become the study subject of urine and stool production, and was immersed in doctors, nurses, medications, blood pressure checks, and vital sign monitoring.

While I felt reduced to a number, I also realized that my

roommate was just 22-B to me. Here we were, two people sharing space at very difficult times with very little connection. The polyester curtain pulled between us divided our illnesses and our lives.

We seemed like zoo animals as the doctors paraded in to observe us in our confinement. The noises of surrounding machines droned on and on as we kept to our own curtain defined cages.

They continued to remove my extra fluid with IV Lasix and albumin transfusions. I developed infections, my muscles deteriorated on my legs and arms, and I felt very weak. I had lost a great deal of weight and most of my hair.

It was ironic that although I went to the hospital to get better, the stay always seemed to bring a host of new problems. My month in the hospital resulted in one disaster cascading into another.

One day as they were trying to remove extra fluid from my body with an albumin transfusion and IV Lasix—extra fluid collected in my lungs. I was gasping for air, and doctors were frantically trying to determine if I had a collapsed lung or blood clots. Something was clearly wrong.

Literally and figuratively, I was drowning in myself: drowning in the fluid that was trapped in my lungs; drowning in my existence; drowning in this disease that was pulling me into the depths of the water and refusing to let go as I struggled to come to the surface; drowning in self pity and longing for my past.

Emergency x-rays came back abnormal and lung specialists were brought in. I couldn't breathe or speak. I was fighting for air and I was terrified.

Dr. Brown came in and took immediate action. He ordered a rapid stop to the albumin transfusions, increased the IV Lasix, and the fluid was soon eliminated from my lungs.

Soon after, my hemoglobin dropped unexpectedly and I received two pints of blood. In 1987, there was a great deal of public confusion and concern over contracting Aids. Therefore, the blood transfusions frightened us.

My mom called the blood bank to learn the risk of getting Aids from a blood transfusion. She was told 1 in 2,000,000. She then recruited her friends to start our own private little blood bank.

Her incredible friends donated blood on my behalf. Once again, kindness illuminated the love and support of the amazing people in our lives.

The hospitalization events continued and I started to have IV problems. The prednisone was making my veins small and uncooperative for all the necessary pokes and prods. Blood draw vampires kept coming in to my room to shove their needles into my veins.

Once, twice, three times…no luck. Poke after poke felt like abuse. On the fourth time the technician got it in, and said that next time he would call anesthesia because I was such a difficult case.

The next lab technician came and struggled to get the needle in my vein. It was the straw that broke the camels back for me. Huge teardrops streamed down my cheeks as he whittled away at me to get the needle placed.

He came back later, popped his head in the door and sweetly said, "Excuse me Jennifer…Hi. I'm the guy who made you cry, and I wanted you to know I am so sorry."

Then a nurse bounded into my room and said I had not urinated enough in the day and my potassium level was high. This is dangerous because elevated potassium can disrupt heart rhythm. Doctors were called immediately.

My mom and dad came to the hospital in the middle of the night and fell asleep in the cramped and uncomfortable hospital room with me.

My mom crawled into my bed, and we were awakened every three hours as blood draws were taken. My potassium kept rising, so the nurse rushed in with Kayexalate, a smelly dark brown fluid that I was required to drink.

It was gritty and thick as oil. I forced it down it. It almost made me throw up, yet it pulled potassium out of my system and another crisis was under control.

This month long hospital stay was a long stretch of boredom mixed with unpleasantness and mindless television. I created a pseudo-schedule to propel myself through the day—as if I was a busy executive with a series of appointments. It starts with lab work, a light breakfast, and a slow, awkward unsatisfying shower.

Time for the maid (well, nurse) to change my linens, short walk around the floor with IV pole in tow, settle in for some local talk show, CNN—what's this—lunch, already? Another walk, phone calls to friends, visit from my mom, read, nap, almost time for Oprah, then the evening news.

Oh where has the day gone? It's dinnertime. (Room service is so nice.) Doctors and nurses pop in to interrupt the busy schedule. Dad stops in. Friends visit. Prime time. David Lettermen… more CNN …and a few unintentionally hilarious infomercials round out the day. Over and over and over.

CHAPTER THIRTEEN

After a long hospital stay, I was planning to go home after one more weekend of observation. Monday came and I was very disappointed. My weight had gone up 2.4 pounds since the day before and my labs were elevated as well.

Dr. Brown was worried I was not stable. He wanted to "observe" me longer. Then he suggested I start on medications to prevent heart disease from the high cholesterol level.

He lined up a heart specialist for me, and casually mentioned the side effects of medication to protect my heart could cause liver function problems.

"Stop it! Stop it!" I thought. "I cannot take on kidney, heart, and liver issues all together." My mind and emotions were blown. I lost it and fell into another all consuming sob session.

The next day came—Tuesday, March 8, 1988—and no hospital discharge. The pull-off-the-date calendar on my wall was just a painful reminder; days were passing and I still could not leave this place!

I was sick of being in that bed and the sickly blue hospital robe. I was sick of the repulsive smells and sterile, impersonal surroundings. I had gained 2.6 pounds of fluid since the day earlier, which was on top of the 2.4 pounds from the day before that. The fluids were building up again.

I was on a fluid/protein/cholesterol/sodium/potassium-restricted diet. Yum. A dietician came into my room one evening with a bowl of peppermint candies. She claimed she could not provide enough calories with my extremely limited diet, so she wanted me to suck on several red and white round discs of sugar energy.

My blood protein level dropped so fast after the albumin transfusion that the doctors were puzzled. With traces of sorrow in his face, Dr. Brown candidly told me, "It is never a good thing to be such a fascinating patient."

More albumin transfusions were planned, and at this rate I thought I might live my whole life in the hospital. I listened constantly to Carly Simon's "Coming Around Again," focusing on the words as though they might set my course.

At the end of the song children sing the well known nursery rhyme, "The itsy bitsy spider climbs up the water spout, out comes the rain and washed the spider out, out comes the sun and dries up all the rain, and the itsy bitsy spider climbs up the spout again."

Illness washed me out. I was praying for the sun so I too, could climb up the spout, and come around again.

CHAPTER FOURTEEN

I visualized a pure white light surrounding my kidneys encircled in a sapphire and emerald green healing band. If powerful thoughts and images could have healed me, my kidneys would have been perfect.

I had another biopsy and the results showed more progression of kidney damage. There was not much hope left that this disease was going to improve from the aggressive prednisone treatment. My kidneys were failing fast.

Various doctors disagreed about alternate medications that could possibly help me, and possibly hurt me. I heard more about risk/benefit analysis then I wanted to, but it turns out medicine is all about the risks and benefits.

"Medications are either placebos or poisons," explained Dr. Brown.

It disarmed me to hear doctors discussing my "quality of life." I was only twenty-three and the quality of my life was up for discussion? How did this happen?

A couple doctors were discussing if I should take a powerful medication called cytoxin. Then one night a resident came into my room, closed the door, sat down, and told me with intensity that I should not take it.

He thought it would be a big mistake and it would not work. I had an emotional outburst and screamed at him "Are you a nephrologist?!!" He said no and I demanded he get out of my room.

Since he was not one of the kidney specialists, his closed-door-words confused and disturbed me. It was definitely out of character for me to scream at a doctor and ask him to leave my hospital room. I think he wrote it off to my huge dose of prednisone, hysteria, and stress.

Dr. Brown told me the results from the prednisone therapy were not as he had hoped. Now it was time to go for broke. The last attempt was a higher dose of prednisone to see if it had any effect on the proteinuria. I had to take an 80-mg. dose, divided into a 20-mg. dose four times a day. This was a hefty amount for my small body.

Nauseous, further hair loss, muscle deterioration, chipmunk cheeks, tremors, voice weakness, fast heartbeat, high blood pressure—this dose completely hammered me.

This high dosage also resulted in a host of other prescriptions necessary to counter the side effects. So high blood pressure medicine, anti-ulcer medications, antacids after every meal, and blood thinning shots that caused multiple bruises were just icing on the medication cake.

I knew I was in for a ride when I asked Dr. Brown how long I would be on this hefty dose of prednisone. He said somberly, "As long as you can tolerate it."

I often wonder how much a body can tolerate. My brother used to reassure me by pointing out all the rock stars that abused heavy drugs for years. "Look at Eric Clapton" he said, "he was a major heroin addict and he looks great."

Pounded by prescription drugs and living to tell the tale. Rock on.

CHAPTER FIFTEEN

Much confusion. Not much improvement. My parents realized I was heading down a dark path. Although we greatly respected Dr. Brown, we felt a visit to the Mayo Clinic in Rochester, Minnesota would be worthwhile.

We had so many theories and we wanted the Mayo Clinic to render the final verdict. Next stop Rochester—the place of second opinions and desperation mixed with hope.

We went looking to find our somewhere-over-the-rainbow diagnosis. I was secretly envisioning some Mayo Clinic expert would see something no one else could see. I wanted a wizard to wave a magic medical wand so I could resume my normal life.

At this point, I was a shell of my former self. I wore a scarf over my head to hide significant hair loss, and it was difficult to walk because I was so weak. It is amazing what a difference a few months can make after you travel through medical hell.

We stayed in the Kaiser Hotel at Mayo, and showed up on time in the main lobby of the enormous clinic. The front desk receptionist looked up my appointments and gave me a series of cards that listed the plethora of tests I was to have done. It was cold and impersonal.

I looked at the woman who handed me my schedule and realized I was just one of many sick people that she provided a schedule to day after day. This was her job. People like me came with hope for their life. She came for a paycheck.

How differently we experienced this same space. The contrast startled me, and I felt again there were two sides to life, and I was on the wrong side.

After a full day of various procedures I was scheduled to see Dr. Donadio, the nephrologist I had envisioned as my Wizard of Oz. All the tests were done and my mom, dad, and I sat in his office and awaited his analysis.

He was in his mid 50's, a fit man with a receding gray hairline and a friendly expression. He looked serious but accessible. I felt comfortable in his office, although it was the typical Mayo clinic ambiance—mossy green, sterile, utilitarian.

I saw a hopeful look in the eyes of my parents before he spoke. It was so difficult to watch their expressions as we trudged through this process. They did not want the promise of their daughter's future to evaporate before their eyes.

Dr. Donadio started with friendly banter. Put-us at-ease kind of talk—good bedside manner, but I was exhausted and not up for clever conversation.

He then looked at the reports and said bluntly "Jennifer, you are a very sick girl. Your kidneys are damaged and they cannot be repaired. You will need to go on dialysis and have a kidney transplant."

That was it. The diagnosis was fired like a bullet; I felt it blast through me as it conclusively shattered my prior self-concept.

I felt like giving up right then and there. Where was the room for hope in that? It sounded like a death sentence to me.

My parents' eyes dropped. I felt I had let them down. How could I have done this to them? How could my body have done this to me?

Dr. Donadio was not done. "Jennifer, you probably feel horrible right now. Your arms and legs are wasted away and you are very weak. Your body is filled with toxic medications and you are experiencing some major side effects from prednisone."

"You will get off this medication and get so much stronger," he continued. "Your hair will grow back and you will feel so much better when you are on dialysis. This is the worst of it now. You are on your way to feeling better."

He helped me consider that part of why I felt so flattened was due to medications rather than illness. I longed to feel better so I attached to his words with all my might. *This is the worst of it now. You are on your way to feeling better.*

As we stepped out his office door, he saw the wheelchair parked outside. He said, "You know I have seen people so weakened from medications that they needed to be wheeled to my office. Good luck to you."

He did not realize the wheelchair was mine. I sat down and my parents wheeled me away.

We returned to the front lobby and hugged each other. My dad had tears in his eyes and said quietly, "I think it will all turn out okay."

My voice cracked, my eyes reddened, I fought back the fear, and said in a weak voice "It has to."

On the drive home from the Mayo Clinic, the three of us were quiet and exhausted as music from the radio played. Bob Marley sang "Three Little Birds," and his voice filled our space as he rhythmically convinced us not to worry about a thing.

"I like this song," my dad said softly. "I think this guy is right." My mom and I smiled wearily for the first time since we left Mayo, and we all allowed Bob Marley to sooth our souls.

CHAPTER SIXTEEN

We returned home with the news that a transplant was inevitable. My mom made calls, and I heard her explaining what the doctor said over and over to friends and family. Her voice was saturated with sadness and concern.

We then made a decision to cry for the whole entire day, and that is what we did. Together, we futzed around the house and just kept crying and crying.

We grieved together for the loss of my health. Yet, I replayed in my mind Dr. Donadio's promise of better days ahead. His words armed my fragile constitution so I could keep on fighting.

To prepare for dialysis I needed to have a vascular access placed so my blood could be accessed and cleaned by an artificial kidney. I had a surgical procedure to get an AV fistula, in which a surgeon connected an artery in my left forearm to a vein.

This connection causes more blood to flow through the vein thereby making it larger. The larger vein and arterial access allow large dialysis needles to be placed to remove and return blood via the dialysis machine.

I was sedated for this procedure, but was not put under. Midway through, I told the nurse and doctor I felt a sudden pain in my chest. The doctor freaked out, "I may have punctured her lung. God damn it! These goddamn nephrotics have shitty veins. Goddamn nephrotic!"

The blood pressure cuffed squeezed my arm and the nurse said, "Her blood pressure is really high." Of course it was high—the doctor was screaming that I was a god damn nephrotic! My lung was not punctured and the pain subsided, but his outburst continued to pierce me.

Like the elephant man's plea, "I am not an animal!," I wanted to bellow, "I am not a goddamn nephrotic!"

In November, I felt puffy in Seattle. By June, I was on dialysis in Minneapolis. Dr. Brown said I was ready and my labs indicated end stage kidney failure.

I was scheduled to start outpatient dialysis treatments at Abbott hospital. A compassionate social worker named Sue gave my mom and me a tour. I had ordered a wig by this point because my hair was mostly gone.

My mom's friend Carol recommended a place in New York, and I bought a sassy brunette pull-on-hairdo from a catalog. I wore a scarf over it so the only "hair" that was visible was bangs and a ponytail. This made me feel less wiggy.

Sue took me through the dialysis unit and introduced me to the technicians. I tried to be cool as she casually showed me around. It was routine to her but I was unsettled to see many seated elderly people attached to plastic tubes and whirling machines.

The tubes filled with blood as the machines spun and churned, and sent the purified blood back into each patient. Everywhere I looked I saw blood—chair after chair of blood filled plastic lines and friendly wrinkled faces. Surely this was not a place for me.

With sudden panic I looked at Sue, "Bathroom?" She pointed, I ran. I just made it into the restroom in time to throw up in the toilet.

Carol, (my go-to wig resource) had breast cancer and was going through her own medical maze. She had been one of my mom's best friends since high school and had an undeniably beautiful spirit. She always lit up the room with her quick wit and contagious sense of fun.

We talked about our illnesses, hair loss, and carrying on. She had recurrent breast cancer after a double mastectomy, yet she seemed to be at peace without fear. She asked me if I was scared. I told her I just didn't know when to give up on the idea that I might get better.

"You never give up on the idea of getting better Jennifer. Never." she said with calm certainty.

So dialysis began. Three times a week I would come to the unit and sit in the faux-leather vinyl reclining chair. Two large needles were inserted into my left forearm by a technician, settings were adjusted, buttons were pushed, pumps would start spinning, and my blood would travel through one needle into a plastic line leading to an artificial kidney.

After the blood was filtered, it was returned through a tube leading to the second needle in my arm. Within two hours, approximately seven pounds of fluid and toxins were removed from my small frame.

My mom and I decided in the midst of all that was happening— we needed a puppy. So we drove to a breeder's farm in northern Minnesota and picked out a cute little Wheaten Terrier. We named her Mickey. She was a soft, sweet, adorable distraction.

During another hospital stay, an intern came in to ask (once again) about the history. My mom was visiting and sat by the bed as he started to examine me. He looked in my ears and exclaimed with excitement, "They look just like the ears in my textbook!"

He was obviously very young and quite sweet. He seemed earnest—like a good student with a *Doogie Howser* appeal. I started answering his questions about my medical history as he was carefully taking notes. For some reason, the whole situation struck me funny.

"I was twenty-two and I started to feel puffy" I said with a subtle smirk. "Then they put me on large doses of prednisone" I continued with slightly visible amusement. I looked at my mom and she was averting her eyes and fighting a smile.

"And then" I said struggling to speak and hold back laughter at the same time, "I had kidney failure."

He looked uncomfortable as he asked me "How long was it after your first symptoms until you went on dialysis?"

I couldn't contain myself anymore as I blurted, "six months" followed by an outburst of unexplained hilarity.

At this point, my mom also let it fly. Like young girls trying to hold it in during church, there was no way for us to contain our inappropriate laughter any longer.

This poor intern didn't quite know what to do, but our howling infected him. He also started laughing...and apologizing.

"I am sorry, this is not a funny story, but you are both laughing," he said with a bewildered mix of concern and amusement. The three of us just continued to laugh, and cut through the predicament with a merry moment shared—in the midst of just another day in the hospital.

CHAPTER SEVENTEEN

After Nick finished his undergraduate credits, he went to London for a post-graduate get away before he settled into "real" life. We had been dating for many years, so we both welcomed a little break. We did not realize kidney failure loomed on the horizon.

While he was in London we shared many letters and phone calls throughout the ordeal. I missed him and all my past he represented. He made me laugh, and laughing made me feel better. He promised he would stay with me, and he talked about "us" and how it would work out.

When his London experience was coming to a close, he was unsure of his next step. He offered to come to Minneapolis and live with me at my parents' home. I was so glad he was coming—if I couldn't be in Seattle, a big piece of my Seattle was coming to me.

He stayed with me and brought some of my social energy back. We called my friends and I went out more. His sense of humor meshed well with my mom's good nature and we had fun.

Yet trouble was brewing. Nick did not like to go to the dialysis unit to sit with me because it made him feel uneasy. I also had a temporary subclavian line placed for dialysis needle access that I had to tuck underneath my shirt when I was not at dialysis. This also made him uncomfortable, and he thought people would look at me like I was a "freak."

Was I a freak? His medical squirms heightened my self-consciousness and made me sad. There was so much to deal with and it was difficult for both of us.

He started going to parties without me and would come home drunk. He felt restless, helpless, and to top it off—confused about his sexuality. Things were getting a little tricky.

My Seattle friend Ryan came to visit me with his friend for a few days, and we went out with Nick and had a few drinks downtown. It was great to see Ryan, and he and his friend stayed with us at my parents' home.

After Ryan landed back in Seattle he called me right away. He said we had to talk about Nick. He told me Nick made a pass at him the night we went out for drinks and he thought I should know.

I felt a strange combination of feelings—I was not surprised—and simultaneously shocked. It was clear that Nick was struggling with so many things and I did not have the energy to sort it out with him.

Selfishly, I needed to focus my energy on my health. I also knew he needed to sort out his own issues in an environment more supportive than I could provide. I asked him to leave.

He begged me to let him stay. He said he couldn't afford to live anywhere else. I told him that was an insufficient reason and he would have to find another resource other than my parents. After considerable drama, my family bought him a plane ticket back to Seattle and our relationship was over. Just like that, another piece of Seattle was gone from my life.

That night, I had a disturbing dream. Remember the classic wooden paddleball toy? A wooden paddle had a ball attached by an elastic string, and the goal was to see how many times you could bounce the rubber ball off the paddle.

I dreamed I was the ball, attached to the world with an elastic string. The world kept propelling me off its surface. I felt completely rejected—not just by my body's betrayal—I felt rejected by the world.

CHAPTER EIGHTEEN

Antsy and unsettled, I decided to move back to Seattle while I was waiting on the transplant list for a kidney. My mom was worried. I was determined. I convinced myself that if I returned to Seattle, I could reclaim my life.

I moved into a house with Lisa and Cindy, assisted by the emotional and financial support of my parents. I signed up for communication classes at the University of Washington. I went to parties and out with friends. I reconnected.

I met with a social worker so I could be placed at a dialysis treatment facility. He told me about a unit that was fairly close to our house. He warned me, however, that prison inmates with kidney failure dialyzed there—so it was a tough crowd.

He also said I could try peritoneal dialysis, which involves filling your abdomen with a large amount of fluid through a tube. The peritoneum in the abdomen acts as the membrane that exchanges the fluids and toxins.

The significant drawback was that my abdomen could become very distended, and he explained it was possible that I would appear pregnant. Although it is a very good option for many dialysis patients, I tuned out immediately when I heard "pregnant."

What a choice—hang out with prison inmates or alter my

appearance so I would look permanently pregnant?!

I found an acceptable dialysis center near the University of Washington and I started to have my treatments there. My plan to "reclaim" my life, however, was failing. I felt more alone then ever and called my mom in tears many times.

I wanted things to be like they were—but things were not the same, and this became painfully clear. I felt sad. I was smacked with the reality my life had changed dramatically.

One afternoon, I was alone at our house and a Kodak commercial appeared on the television. The first image showed a dad dancing with his daughter at her wedding. She was a beautiful bride, fresh faced, young, happy and healthy. Her dad warmheartedly remembers images of her growing up.

Scenes flashed of his daughter as an adorable baby, in kindergarten class, at elementary school, playing softball, navigating teenage years. The scene returned to the dad and daughter dancing at her wedding.

Her eyes twinkle as he revisits the milestones leading to this moment of passage. A sweet song plays over the series of images with the chorus of "Daddy's Little Girl."

That commercial *unhinged* me. It stabbed me with the concept of what I thought my life was supposed to be. I wanted my life to resemble the 30-second snapshot of life created by Kodak. I sobbed for hours.

My mind flooded with my memories of the little girl I used to be. The little girl that ran to the back door when my dad came home from work so I could step on his feet as he walked me back into the kitchen.

I became nostalgic with memories of my little girl self that loved my mom's cinnamon toast and tater tot casserole; went everywhere with my Peggy doll; and waited with excitement for my Nancy Drew books to come in the mail (via my Nancy Drew book club membership, of course).

I longed to naively reside in the safe bubble of childhood my parents had once created for me. What happened to that once carefree girl in pigtails?

CHAPTER NINETEEN

I faced the fact that Seattle was not the best place for me considering the circumstances, so I returned to Minneapolis and continued to wait for a kidney. The United Network of Organ Sharing (UNOS) manages this list of people waiting for an organ. When a kidney becomes available it is reported to UNOS and the organization matches the medical characteristics of the available organ with those that are waiting to receive a kidney.

Many people think you rise to the top of the list, but it does not work quite like that. When an available organ is entered into the system, a ranked list is generated from potentially suitable recipients.

The criteria that determine this ranking includes blood type, tissue match, time on the list, antibody levels, degree of medical urgency, and the distance between the available organ and the recipient.

The first person on the ranked list is not always able to receive the kidney. The matched person must be "healthy" and ready for immediate surgery. If the first ranked recipient has the flu for example, he or she is ruled out and the kidney would go to the next suitable recipient.

Dr. Brown briefly discussed the idea of a family member donating a kidney to me. Although my dad and Steve did not have compatible blood types, my mom and I both had blood type A. We had a simple blood test that determined my mom and I did not have enough matching antigens. I went on the list and was given a beeper so I could be notified in the event a match was found.

I moved into an apartment in Minneapolis part-time with Rachael and her boyfriend Mike. The apartment was close to the dialysis unit so after my treatments on Mondays, Wednesdays, and Fridays, I would go to our shared apartment.

Rachael and I had been friends since junior high, and she has always been one of my favorite people. She is a curvy blonde with curly hair, small in stature, and big in personality.

Rachael grew up in a home that was half Jewish and half Catholic. When young, my friends and I envied her good fortune to celebrate both Hanukah and Christmas. Somehow, Rachael always carried celebration with her, and her nurturing nature and refined cooking skills always enriched my time with her. She convinced me there was more to my life than dialysis and medical appointments, and I could have fun with friends despite everything else. Living with Rachael was like settling into a warm, comforting hug.

Mike and Rae met at the University of Minnesota where Mike was completing a degree in business. His dark hair, tall athletic build, and sharp wit were a perfect compliment to Rae's special qualities.

Mike reliably supplied the apartment with Diet Cokes and movie rentals, and the three of us hunkered in and hung out. I would usually get home late from dialysis after Rae and Mike had already eaten dinner.

A typical post-dialysis evening consisted of my microwave Lean Cuisine, Rae's efforts to supplement my frozen dinner with a gourmet salad, and the three of us plopping on the couch to watch television.

The apartment was not in a safe neighborhood. There was a security camera at the entrance door so we could monitor who was entering the building. Ironically, the security camera was stolen.

The apartment decor was an immersion in brown. Brown building, brown carpet, institution beige walls, and fake brown Formica wood.

Despite the drab surroundings, I loved Rae and Mike's company and friendship. It was clear they were headed to engagement and marriage, and I envied their path. I wanted to be on that path too somehow, yet I felt so far from it.

I was a part of many weddings, however, and was happy to celebrate many wonderful marriages. My friend Kristin and I had been close in college and she had been dating Pete for quite awhile. She called and said they were going to be married and asked if I could be a bridesmaid. I was honored to be a part of her wedding.

Kristen was from Boulder, so I flew to Colorado. I was able to fly out between my Friday and Monday dialysis sessions. Cell phones were not widely available then, so the transplant clinic instructed me to be sure to have my beeper with me at all times. If a kidney became available, I would jump on a plane and come back.

My hemoglobin was stubbornly low so I often required blood transfusions to keep my energy up. I was very anemic right before the wedding, so after my dialysis run I topped off with a couple new pints of blood, headed to the airport and was off.

My hair was growing in but looked unwieldy so I invested in a hair weave to bridge the difference. With my glossy brunette weave and forest green velvet bridesmaid dress ready to go, I looked and felt like a normal girl. Plus, my energy was up from my freshly acquired new red blood cell cocktail.

I met a medical student at the wedding, and he was fascinated with my recent experiences. I told him about my fluid restriction and showed him a pamphlet that outlined my dietary and fluid plan. We were amused that the printed recommendation for alcohol consumption said to consume shots in order to drink less fluid.

"Doctor's orders. Get the lady some shots!" he shouted with mock authority.

We liked each other and at the end of the night, he kissed me. He tried to put his hand through my hair but it got hung up on my weave. When I told him why I had unusual clumps near my scalp he said "Oh, I just though you used a lot of hair gel." I found this really amusing.

He told me I looked like Winona Ryder, and made me feel like I was still fun and attractive despite my traumatic medical experiences. I flew back to Minneapolis and felt happy.

—

CHAPTER TWENTY

Beth had been living in Portland, Oregon after she finished her undergraduate work at Lewis and Clark College. She decided to move back to Minneapolis and was looking for a roommate.

Beth and I had known each other for years. Our parents were good friends and traveled together, jointly owned a sailboat, and planned family outings. I was also close with Beth's sister Sheila, and spent a lot of time at their home.

They had the go-to house with the pool and pinball machine. As an extra bonus, their pantry was always spilling over with sugary cereal (my dad banned these cereals from our lives after he read *The Sugar Blues*.)

Beth and Sheila's dad was a feisty and entertaining Irish man that made me feel more than welcome, as he boisterously insisted, "Jenny—scoop a bigger helping of those bloody Lucky Charms!"

Rachael and I agreed it was a good idea for me to move into an apartment with Beth, so the apartment hunt began. We found the perfect place near Lake of Isles and scooped it up. I loved that Beth was back in town and the apartment was delightful.

It was built in the early 1900's, and was filled with sunlight. Small and complete—it had a kitchen, dining area, living room and two bedrooms. The rooms were delineated with creamy plaster archways, glass corner dining cabinets, skinny-planked oak floors, and a cheerful ambiance.

I had been seeing an acupuncturist named Judith, and she taught me about the subtle powers of the color pink. Her treatment room was a whisper soft shade, and I always felt so relaxed there. This room and the feeling it evoked inspired me to paint my apartment bedroom pink as well (with the hesitant approval of my landlord).

I bought a richly detailed floral rug, a traditional French baker's rack for shelving and display, and high thread count dive-into-me bedding. I felt good here. I felt like a real life was underway.

Real life despite the fact I needed to be hooked up to a dialysis machine three times a week to stay alive. I became accustomed to my routine. I often woke up, felt nauseous, threw up, and then carried on with my day.

I had strict limitations on what I ate and drank, and still had to carefully monitor my fluid ounces, potassium milligrams, phosphorus milligrams, and sodium.

The fluid restriction was a big challenge because I was extremely thirsty all day long. To manage my unquenchable thirst I sucked on ice cubes and chewed sour lemon gum. It was important to limit fluids because I could become fluid overloaded quickly due to zero urine output. (It is a very strange feeling when you don't ever pee.)

Like a dieter that becomes obsessed with food, I became obsessed with fluids. I had a recurring dream that I was drinking gallons and gallons of ice water, and would wake up terrified that I had exceeded my fluid limit.

I had always been a healthy eater and loved fruits and vegetables. Unfortunately most fruits and vegetables are high in potassium, so I had to restrict them to prevent heart irregularities and serious complications.

The high phosphorus levels found in dairy products can compromise bone health, so these had to be avoided as well.

It was all a delicate balance, and I carefully complied with my meal and fluid plan. It was a seemingly normal life, but I knew I was far from the life I thought I would have at 24 years old.

The social worker at the dialysis unit recommended I see a psychologist to assist me with my adjustment. "Perfect" I thought, "I would love to learn how to 'adjust' to a damaged life."

Ida was a short, thick, crabby woman with a strong European accent. She had an array of opinions—some good, some not so good. One of her unusual ideas was that I should attend AA meetings.

"Why?" I asked confused. "I don't have a problem with alcohol."

"Ahhh, but you do have a drinking problem," she said, looking quite pleased with her clever insight. "You are fluid restricted, and those in AA are alcohol restricted. You share a common bond."

Needless to say, I did not seek out an AA meeting. It would have been hard to explain that I felt remorse for having two tall glasses of ice water instead of two small shots of vodka.

We talked about my stalled career as I explained to her that I did "nothing."

She responded directly, "Jennifer, dialysis is not nothing. This procedure is keeping you alive and takes up a lot of time and energy. Don't belittle yourself—you are doing quite a bit more than most ever will need to do to stay healthy."

A few sessions later I told Ida I had adjusted, thanked her, and never saw her again. I agreed with her assessment, dialysis was something. But it was not enough—I was desperate to work like any other twenty-something college graduate.

I was fresh out of school with a business degree, public relations experience, and filled with ideas and ambition. I had been so pleased and proud of the letter of reference I received from the Internship Director at Cole & Weber. "Jennifer is a rising star in the field of public relations, and is one to watch."

I was now far from one to watch in the field of public relations—more like one to watch on a pathetic medical drama. I just did not see how it was possible to get a job with my dialysis schedule and unpredictable health.

CHAPTER TWENTY-ONE

My dad sympathized with my situation and offered to hire me at his custom home building company. He created a position for me to generate company communications and put to use some of my public relations and business skills.

So I gratefully started working at L. Cramer Company. I created an internal staff newsletter that was basically a morale booster. It was fun and generated good will.

I also created a client newsletter that generated calls and was a success. From here I worked with the advertising agency that placed and designed L. Cramer's advertisements. I learned so much more about advertising and public relations, and it was exciting to feel like I was actually a part of the business world.

As a team, we created a corporate brochure, hiring models, an arrogant photographer, copywriters, and printers. It was an expensive project for a small company, and the piece turned out beautifully. All of us involved were happy it received a Marketing and Merchandising Award of Excellence.

I was still wearing my wig, but I kept it hidden with a scarf-of-the-day. The artistic director for the brochure told me she liked my scarves. I explained to her why I wore them (thinking she probably knew already). She did not know, so then I felt embarrassed and awkward.

It was difficult to know what to say to people. Working for my dad's company, most everyone knew about my health situation. But on larger projects where outside professionals were involved, I felt highly self-conscious. Do they think I am strange? Are they staring at me? I worried about how people perceived me.

I sent out press releases for the company, and we achieved increased publicity and good press. I did whatever needed to be done—answered phones, paid bills and collected rents from tenants (my dad owned the building.) I developed building budgets, and started to track prospective client communications. It wasn't exactly what I had expected to be doing at this stage, but it was a job and gave me a purpose.

All the while, dialysis continued on Mondays, Wednesdays, and Fridays.

The nurses and technicians at the unit were really wonderful people, and my fellow patients were a colorful group. The dialysis unit became my second office and my second life. In addition to the essential blood cleaning, I found surprising comfort in the camaraderie.

One day I was sitting in the small waiting room close to the entrance of the unit. They were often backed up so it was a rare event to start at my designated time.

Eventually, Jerry the technician called my name as if I was a contestant on the Price Is Right. "Jennifer Cramer...come on down!" I stood up and spontaneously tap danced down the center aisle to get to my chair. Applause cheered me on as I displayed comically bad tap dancing skills.

Olga was an older woman in her eighties and offered her own unique brand of entertainment. She had a deeply lined face with mousy brown hair—thin and teased—a gravel-filled smoker's voice, and a sharp tongue. Olga was loud, boisterous, and always excited to see me.

One day she spontaneously barked while we were both in our dialysis chairs, bloodlines running through our machines, "Jennifer, you are a cute kid. I hope you don't get murdered."

Puzzled and amused, I laughed along with the nearby nurses and technicians. Olga was frequently spewing out crazy comments.

Another day, Mark, a young dialysis technician was placing the needles in my fistula arm and Olga spouted, "Jennifer, you should marry Mark, you know...his dad's a *dentist*."

Olga loved Tom the technician. Tom was a strawberry blonde athletic man in his early thirties. He was very knowledgeable, and had a confident presence in the unit. Tom seemed to be in charge, and he did not doubt his skills. Some fistulas were more difficult to stick than others, and Olga had a tough one.

If someone had weak veins, the fistula could infiltrate, leading to a big bruise that bumped up on the arm like a small plum. An infiltration hurt, so it was something to be avoided. Olga always pleaded for Tom to insert her needles, and he was always there for her.

Olga was uniquely endearing. We were worlds apart—it seemed unlikely I would have befriended her in a typical circumstance. Yet, we shared time at this dialysis unit and became positively linked through negative circumstances.

CHAPTER TWENTY-TWO

When my hair first started coming back, it was wiry and redder than before. I went to see Henry my hairstylist and he recommended stimulating oils to rub into my scalp and condition my newfound growth.

Henry always had overflowing enthusiasm, so I loved going to see him. He had a flair for hair and a zest for life. He would tell me what he made for dinner the night before with so much excitement—I could almost see and smell his vegetable stir-fry with crisp broccoli. He put more drama into dinner than anyone else I knew.

He cut hair in a small studio, one client at a time. As he was rubbing the oil into my scalp, my fuzzy hair was sticking up like cotton candy. His next client was new to his studio, walked in, saw me, and looked terrified.

"Oh no Henry, I think she is going to bolt before you get to her next." I whispered. We giggled at the thought that he had created my special look.

Minneapolis was beginning to feel like home again, as my high school friends started to return one by one. My longtime Golden Valley friend Amy had started to date my college friend Ned, and this connected both my worlds.

I met Ned in Tacoma and he was in Nick's fraternity. Ned grew up in Orono, and went to high school with Susan. Ned moved back to Minneapolis from Tacoma, and Amy moved back home from New Mexico. Ned couldn't resist Amy's pretty face with perfect dimples, and Amy was drawn to Ned's established country club background—remixed with a laid back urban vibe.

Mike and Rachael were still together, and Beth had a boyfriend named Daniel. Daniel was brooding with dark hair, powder pale skin, and a softly intense manner. He was vampire-esque before it was the thing to be, and had just earned a most un-manly degree in Women's Studies.

Carrie had recently graduated from Madison, Wisconsin, and was back in town. We affectionately called her "chicken legs" (after a drunken customer bellowed at her while she was a waitress at Embers during high school).

Fact of the matter is—as awkward as the nickname "chicken legs" sounds—Carrie is a 5'11" honey blonde that could pass as a super-model. She was close friends with Peyter, another University of Puget Sound graduate, and an Orono high school friend of Ned's.

Liz was back from Colorado (where her skin became more tan, her hair became more blonde, and her essence took on a mountain-loving flair). She was dating another Puget Sound SAE fraternity brother from Puget Sound named Markham.

How unlikely was it that so many of my Minneapolis friends had Puget Sound boyfriends, except me? It was great almost all of us (except Suzanne who was in San Francisco) were happily together again.

In 1989, the movie *Steel Magnolias* was showing in theaters. It was a based on a popular play, and the story revolves around a group of women that share friendship and their lives. Julia Roberts plays a young woman who has kidney failure and requires dialysis. Her mom, played by Sally Fields, donates her kidney to the Julia Roberts character, so she can have a kidney transplant.

My mom and I saw the movie together. It was billed as a dramatic comedy. Drama yes, but it was a bit close to our situation to occupy the place of comedy. Amy saw it and said, "Wow…Steel Magnolias is just like your life!" I told her I hoped not, being that Julia Roberts rejects her kidney, goes into a coma, and dies at the end.

She looked horrified and started to backtrack. I laughed and told her it was okay—I knew what she meant. We agreed it was the dialysis part that was similar and left it at that. (I had secretly hoped she meant I was the spitting image of Julia Roberts.)

I knew my future was unpredictable. Yet one day at dialysis I had an abrupt lesson that no one can predict his or her future. Tom (Olga's favorite technician) was not there. Young Tom. Healthy Tom. Fit Tom. Tom seemingly had his life in front of him, and his days were devoted to helping those of us that were ill. Suddenly, Tom had a brain aneurism and died.

Life does not make sense. Tom's surprising death was a severe lesson that life is black and white. I was not less alive because I had kidney failure and was on dialysis. I was every bit as alive as anyone else, and I learned to focus on appreciating everyday I had.

CHAPTER TWENTY-THREE

Despite my job and reactivated social life, I was still unsatisfied with my career progress. So I decided to pursue a Master's degree in Business at The University of St. Thomas in St. Paul, Minnesota. I wanted to learn more, absorb more, see more, study more—I was still hungry for business.

The first step was to complete the GMAT entrance exam. The day of the exam I was too sick to drive myself. My mom drove me to the test location and I threw up in the car. Nauseous and exhausted, I somehow managed to get through it and was accepted to the program.

There was a catch. The program required two years of job experience, and I had one and a half. I was accepted on a deferred basis after I met the requirement of six months of additional time on the job.

Six months felt like an eternity, and I cried and cried and cried. I flung myself on my old bed at my parents' house—sobbing out of control, feeling certain that my life was forever in neutral. My dad came in and reassured me the time would pass and it would be okay. Despite his wisdom, I felt doomed.

I wanted something good to happen now—I did not want to have to wait for one more thing. I started to get so tired of going to dialysis. I was on the transplant list but it seemed it would never happen. The wait started to feel unbearable.

PART TWO

Better to light a candle than to curse the darkness.
-Chinese Proverb-

CHAPTER TWENTY-FOUR

And then it happened. The phone call came. It was March 5, 1990, and I was at my parents' house. A man from the University of Minnesota Medical Center called and said there was an available kidney match for me, and asked if I could get to the hospital right away.

I will never forget that call and the look in my mom's eyes. Excitement and fear blended and instantly changed the atmosphere. My brother Steve was home, and we called my dad. I called Beth. I don't know who else was called, but I remember packing my bag and getting strong and powerful hugs. Off we went.

I was overloaded with mixed emotions. On one hand, I felt like a child on Christmas Eve—overflowing with the anticipation of all that was to come. I had invested many thoughts into the rewards of this transplant, and now it was upon me.

Of course I was also nervous about the possibility of the outcome being different that I expected. I swiftly pushed these thoughts aside.

I kept repeating to myself, "Don't worry, you don't have to do any of the work—just go to sleep and wake up."

So that is what I did. I went in, got prepped, got the IV, went to sleep—and three to four hours later I woke up with a new kidney.

I forgot to consider one important thing however. Pain! The first thing I said when I woke up in a medication stupor was, "Nobody told me it would hurt."

Nurses were shouting at me in the recovery room, "Jennifer can you hear me??? Are you awake??? Your kidney is making urine. It started to make urine on the table. On a scale of 1-10 how much does it hurt???"

"A lot!!!"

More morphine was pumped into the IV lines and I faded back into a blurry land with soft edges. Time passed. Soon, I was back in a hospital room, as a team of nurses (skillfully) placed a plastic board under me and slipped me into the bed—I slid over like a fried egg out of a non-stick pan.

My new transplanted kidney was located on the right side of my lower abdomen, and I had a large scar in the shape of a boomerang. It is typical that original kidneys (which are located in the back) are not removed.

I started walking gingerly on day one. By day three I was walking quite well. Slowly but surely. My kidney was producing urine and my creatinine was improving dramatically. (Creatinine is the blood test that measures kidney function.)

A team of doctors and residents came parading into my room soon after my surgery to examine my incision. As I lifted my hospital gown to expose the fresh scar, they stood over me and stared. Beauty is most definitely in the eye of the beholder—as they admired the site, the main resident said, "That is truly lovely."

After a few days, something did not feel right. My urine output slowed way down and my eyes were puffy. I felt an ominous cloud was on the horizon.

I told the doctor I felt swollen and he decided to check my urine for protein. If protein was found in my urine, then focal glomerulosclerosis was back. I already knew the answer.

Sure enough, there was protein in my urine. Normal urine has none, I had 10 grams. Now what? I had been planning that this transplant would be the train ride to my future. Sadly, it appeared that this train would never leave the station.

Dr. Brown said I needed a biopsy to confirm his suspicion.

The biopsy results came back. He walked into my hospital room and told me with sad eyes and visible disappointment, "Your disease has recurred."

He then pumped his fist in the air, raised his usually calm voice, and exclaimed, "I did NOT WANT you to have RECURRENCE."

He talked about some medication options and said our goal was to minimize or slow the disease progression so I could keep the kidney as long as possible.

After four days, I received a dinner pass to go home to my parents' house to get away from hospital food, and eat in a friendlier environment. I sat quietly at the table where I had so many family meals growing up, and slowly moved the chicken and vegetables around my plate with my fork. I felt puffy, depressed, alone, and worried about my life.

What was to become of me now?

I was released from the hospital with a whole new list of drugs to suppress my immune system so I would not reject the kidney. Because the first few weeks after a transplant are critical, I was instructed to report to the Transplant Clinic any spike in temperature, pain over the kidney, increase in weight or blood pressure—anything at all that did not feel right.

I was told to get my labs checked three times a week. My transplant coordinator provided a three-ring binder of all I should know, a list of numbers to call and the hope of improved health.

Friends and family were calling and sending wonderful cards and well-wishes for my long-awaited transplant. But I did not feel deserving of their positive attention. I felt somehow I had messed this up with recurrence. Was I healthy or not? I didn't know.

So many things were much better. I didn't need dialysis. I could eat potassium and phosphorus foods and didn't have to severely restrict my fluids. I just didn't know how long this kidney would last. Six months? Six years?

I was told the kidney came from a young man that was in a car accident in Rochester Minnesota. I thought of his family and their unspeakable loss and then I felt guilty that my body did not receive this gift perfectly. I didn't want to feel so much anymore. I was tired and I wanted to go numb.

CHAPTER TWENTY-FIVE

Dr. Brown started me on some new medications to manage the proteinuria. I was advised that a low protein/low fat diet could prolong the life of my kidney, so low protein/low fat it was.

I voraciously read a book called *The Food Pharmacy*, and learned that the omega 3 fats in tuna were beneficial to slow inflammation. Mustard was also supposed to hinder inflammation—I made tuna and mustard my mission.

I drank apple cider vinegar diluted in water, consumed asparagus, artichokes, watermelon—anything I read about that could improve my health became part of my routine.

I desperately wanted to crack some kind of code that would turn my situation around. Surely there must be a magic combination of tuna and apple cider vinegar that could flip a cellular switch and turn off the autoimmune assault.

Yet, there was no cure for my disease and I was going to have this kidney for an undetermined period of time. Eventually, I realized I had a significant decision to make. I could be swallowed by my situation and be unhappy and depressed—or—I could try to accept it and move forward.

Hope or despair? I chose hope. I simplified my wish list and carried on. My new goal was to make my life the best I could with the circumstances I had. No matter what hand I was dealt, kidney disease or not, dialysis or not, executive career or not, boyfriend or not—my single focus was to appreciate and be grateful for the things I had.

I strived to live by the wise words of Joseph Campbell, "We must be willing to give up the life we've planned so we can live the life that is waiting for us."

I was also inspired by the insights in Shakti Gawain's *Creative Visualization*, and fully embraced her principles of positive imagery and affirmation. I believed if I put positive energy into the universe, I would attract positive energy.

I started imagining the life I wanted, and believed I had the ability to achieve it. The metaphor of life as a river gave me a sense of calm.

The concept is that you should not cling tightly to the riverbank of life. You need to let go and trust life's current to transport you safely along with the river's flow.

I gained acceptance, believed in abundance, and armed myself with affirmations and visualizations. I affirmed, visualized, affirmed, visualized, and focused on positive energy, better health, healing, letting go, optimism, and peace. Positive imagery guided me, calmed me, and propelled me forward.

CHAPTER TWENTY-SIX

B eth was offered an opportunity to travel to China and work at the World Trade Center. I was excited for her as she set out to expand her experiences. I set out find a new apartment.

I loved being close to the signature Minneapolis Lake of the Isles and Lake Calhoun. As I walked along the green grass parkway that bridges these lakes, I often admired flanking beautiful brick apartment buildings.

Although I loved the location, I assumed these choice apartments would be unaffordable. To my great surprise they were very reasonably priced for such a gorgeous location.

I rented a one-bedroom apartment on the second floor that featured the same classic character as the apartment I shared with Beth, and settled in to the first place of my own.

At the time, Dr. Brown was involved in some experimental studies that linked cholesterol reduction with improved kidney function. A systemic byproduct of my protein leak was high cholesterol, so he started treating me with lipidpheresis procedures.

Lipidpheresis was similar to dialysis, but the procedure removed cholesterol from the blood rather than toxins and fluid. I would sit in a hospital bed for a few hours twice a month, as cholesterol was filtered out of my blood and replaced with albumin.

I felt happy and I continued to focus on all the positives:

- I felt grateful that I did not develop kidney problems while I was in college and was able to experience such an ideal college experience.

- I felt grateful I had a fulfilling job.

- I felt grateful so many people loved me.

- I felt grateful I had hair again.

- I felt grateful I could drink delicious fluids.

- I felt grateful I could eat delicious foods.

- I felt grateful for sunny days and beautiful flowers.

- I felt grateful for page turning books.

- I felt grateful for going to see movies.

- I felt grateful I could work out.

- I felt grateful I was working on my M.B.A.

- I felt grateful I could go out on dates.

- I felt grateful I could laugh.

- And most of all, I felt grateful I was alive.

CHAPTER TWENTY-SEVEN

Graduate school began and I started to attend business classes on Tuesday and Thursday evenings after work, as well as Saturdays. I was well advised by a co-worker to find study partners from the start.

I took the advice to heart and quickly befriended Larry, Todd, and Christine. We worked on business projects together and supported each other through long study sessions and assignments.

One of our most noteworthy projects was developing a marketing analysis and strategy for a local business. Many businesses offered to participate in the program, and we were assigned to analyze a day care for elderly patients.

We spent a great deal of time on the assignment and were ready for our presentation. The business owner requested we present the information at his home. As we professionally outlined our research, he pounded cocktail after cocktail with his friend. In record time, they became totally looped. He did not focus on a word we said. All was not lost; at least we received an A from our professor.

Back in Seattle—Susan married Tim, Cindy married Jack, Sarah married Boris, Gillian married Kyle—marriages were popping up right and left.

In Minneapolis, Larry, Todd and I frequently studied at Larry's condo, which is where I eventually met and became friends with

Larry's girlfriend Dawn.

One night Larry picked me up to go to class and said he and Dawn were going to break up. Dawn called me soon after, and asked if there were available apartments in my building.

There was an open spot one floor down and she moved in. Larry's loss was my gain. Dawn and I spent a lot of time together eating, lounging, walking around the lakes, and sharing single life.

We compared opinions about the guys that lived in the apartment and had our fair share of awkward dates. Dawn had an endless lunch-turns-into-roller-blading-turns-into-dinner date from hell; while I went out with a guy who enthusiastically responded to every simple statement I said with "Jeepers Creepers."

CHAPTER TWENTY-EIGHT

One Saturday Dawn went to sunbathe in the Parkway, and I joined her a bit later. She was ready to take a sunbreak and said as she left, "Get the story on that guy hitting golf balls for me. He's cute."

As I looked his way, he walked over and started talking to me. I was in a yellow striped bathing suit and he was wearing navy swim trunks. He was very friendly and covered many topics, his family, his friends, his profession (eating disorder specialist) and working on a Ph.D. at the University of Minnesota.

He asked me if I golfed, I told him no, and he volunteered to show me how to swing a club. He stood behind me, put the club in front of me, and moved my arms in a sample swing. I was acutely aware that my fistula was on display. He didn't say anything about it, so I assumed he was a medical student.

He told me his name was Dirk Miller and he lived in the apartment building next to Dawn and me. We said goodbye, I went inside, found Dawn, and told her all about him.

I learned he grew up in Pennsylvania with his brother and two sisters; small town southeast of Pittsburgh; fanatic Steelers fan; loves to golf; did I mention fanatic Steelers fan? (worth repeating); working on his Ph.D.; specializes in eating disorder treatment; and was our neighbor.

"Wow, you really got a lot of background, " she said.

Dirk stopped by the next day. He buzzed my apartment from the lobby but I was not home. Dawn was leaving and saw him buzzing away. He saw Dawn and asked if she knew where I was—she told him I was out.

"I was going to ask Jennifer out for dinner," he said. He continued (awkwardly and slightly embarrassed—he confessed later) "Well…do you want to go out for dinner?" She said she couldn't go, but she would tell me he stopped by.

Dawn told me the whole story and I said, "That's sweet, Dirk is looking for some new friends."

She shot me a stern glance and said slowly, as if she was teaching me an important lesson, "Listen Jennifer—no straight guy is *ever* going to just want to be your friend." We proceeded to have a *When Harry Met Sally* debate.

The next day Dirk came by, buzzed, and I let him into my apartment. Dawn scolded me again, "You shouldn't just let some stranger buzz their way into to your apartment—what if you let in a serial killer?" Perhaps she had a point.

Dirk asked me out to dinner. We walked down Dean Parkway and stopped at the corner restaurant across from Lake Calhoun. I learned more about him, told him more about me, and had an enjoyable time. And luckily, as far as I could tell—he did not provide any visible clues that he might be a serial killer.

CHAPTER TWENTY-NINE

Lisa called from Seattle with some big news—she was engaged to Mike! Again, I was delighted to be a bridesmaid in a special wedding. This bridesmaid dress was indigo blue linen, sleeveless, and fell just above the knee. It was cute and simple and the intent was (as always) I could wear it again. (Take a guess if I ever wore it again…has anyone ever worn it again?)

Lisa was a beautiful bride. She glowed and her dress made her look like a fairy tale princess. Mike beamed and very eloquently expressed his love for her at their reception dinner.

I looked at Lisa and she broke into a full-fledged squished-up-face overcome-with-emotion cry. I was so happy for her and felt like I was witnessing her happily-ever-after. Would I have mine?

My second date with Dirk was at a downtown restaurant called Chez Bananas. I learned about Dirk's favorite movies, as I (patiently) listened to him recite word for word his favorite lines from *Dirty Harry*.

"I know what you're thinking. Did he fire six shots or only five? Well, to tell you the truth, in all this excitement I kind of lost track myself. But being this is a .44 Magnum, the most powerful handgun in the world, and would blow your head clean off, you've got to ask yourself one question: Do I feel lucky? Well do ya punk?"

"You sweet talker you, I bet you say that to all the girls."

I told Steve about my date with Dirty Harry. Steve (an avid movie buff) was very impressed. "I've got to meet this guy."

On the third date we went back to our neighborhood restaurant. After an early dinner we walked around the block and talked.

I told him I had an undergraduate business degree from the University of Puget Sound, and explained how much I loved the Pacific Northwest. To add some extra polish to my credentials, I told him that the President at Puget Sound referred to our school as the Harvard of the West.

"That's funny," he said, "because I think the President of Harvard refers to their institution as the Puget Sound of the East." Funny and clever…I was intrigued.

On the fourth date we enjoyed Korean food at a restaurant Uptown. Good food, good conversation, good time. His movie references continued.

"You talkin' to me? You talkin' to me? You talkin' to me?"

"I know this one! DeNiro, *Taxi Driver*."

In addition to learning that Dirk was a fan of movies and good food, I found him to be confident, intelligent, ambitious, and attractive. All good things. It was on this date I self-consciously told Dirk I had a kidney transplant.

I thought I was revealing, "I am damaged goods. Defective merchandise." To my surprise, he did not seem visibly put off. (I think I scored by nailing that DeNiro quote.) I felt clean…honest and naked—naked in a good way.

Dirk shared his own story as well. He had seriously struggled with alcohol addiction and had not had a drink in years. I already suspected—the non-alcohol beer he ordered on our first date was a strong clue. We both shared our defects and the world kept spinning.

He asked if I wanted some ice cream. To his amazement, I told him I was not a big fan of ice cream. He pondered this for a second, and said "Okay then, we can arrange it so I'll eat the ice cream and you drink the alcohol."

"That works." I said as we smiled. He reached for my hand and we walked together with the realization that something good was in the air.

I wasn't really expecting anything specific from the relationship. I thought marriage was for my friends and actresses in Kodak commercials. I just delighted in his companionship.

CHAPTER THIRTY

I was still working at my dad's office and things were going well. I started taking on more of a role with the clients, and started assisting my dad with sales. He was a great teacher as he readily shared his wealth of information.

He understands people and frequently claims Dale Carnegie's *How To Win Friends and Influence People* is the best book he has ever read. Steve and I referred to it as the Larry Cramer bible. Growing up, we rolled our eyes as our dad read aloud about stamping out indecision and energetically pounded his feet on the floor for emphasis.

As amusing as this was, my dad did understand the timeless truths found in Dale Carnegie's classic bestseller. He was a master of appreciating people and seeing things from their point of view.

At the office I watched him win friends and influence people, and I learned. He was a skilled businessman and was successful because he focused on people over profits. He earned a solid reputation for being honest, fair, and a man of great integrity.

I honed my relationship development skills and custom home building expertise. I became fully responsible for the marketing and corporate communications, and started to work with clients to manage their projects pre-construction.

I guided them through the coordination of design and specifications, and was enthusiastic about the variety of selections that made each home unique.

Since I was a young girl, I was highly attuned to the power of interior space to captivate and comfort. I frequently rearranged my bedroom furniture, eager to explore the possibilities of changing compositions. I was compelled by the way good design can impart and improve a mood. I found my passion was stirred in the custom home business, and I loved my job.

My dad would introduce me to clients as his daughter. I bristled because I wanted to be regarded as a businesswoman with a valuable set of skills.

In my mind, his introduction reduced me to "she has a chronic illness, there is no where else for her to work, she's my daughter."

One day in frustration, I said, "Why do you have to tell everybody I am your daughter?"

He looked stung and said, "I am very proud that you are my daughter and I just want people to know."

I suddenly felt foolish. Of course he was pleased with my business skills and master's degree work, but he could find those skills in other professionals as well. Family is more special than degrees and achievements, and our family connection was something to be proud of—not something to conceal.

He was right. From that point forward I enthusiastically introduced myself as the daughter of Larry Cramer. And I recognize it is a unique distinction, for I am the only lucky girl that gets to boast with pride that Larry Cramer is my dad.

CHAPTER THIRTY-ONE

Dirk and I continued to have fun as he won me over with his quick wit, sharp intelligence and boyish good looks. We kept busy with restaurants; movies; baseball games; festivals; art fairs; bike rides; hanging out with friends; strong coffees; ice creams for Dirk and drinks for me.

I learned more about where he came from and where he was going. He grew up in a modest home on several acres in the rural setting of Scottdale, Pennsylvania. As a teenager, he busted out of the confines of his religious upbringing and small town via drinking. This hobby offered a quick and easy escape.

At the age of 22, bolstered by the insistence of his concerned parents, he went to an alcohol/drug treatment program. 28 days later, he walked out that door and never had a drink again.

At about the same time, his sister Emily developed anorexia and became emaciated. Very little was known then about eating disorder care, and it was difficult to get treatment. Dirk saw the devastation this psychological disease imposed on his sister and family.

In addition, he was a wrestler in high school, so he knew firsthand the pressure this sport imposed on him and his fellow athletes to make weight. He wanted to make a difference and shine a light on this condition that lurked in the shadows.

So he pursued studies in public health and psychology, and found himself at the University of Minnesota to earn a Ph.D. and advance his expertise in the field of eating disorder treatment.

Dirk is a logical thinker, and his affinity for speed and efficiency were evident soon after I met him. He described his typical thought process as "how to get from A to B in the fastest possible way." This explained his preference for Porsches and plethora of speeding tickets.

One evening Dirk and I were watching television in my apartment. We sat together on my charcoal gray love seat, and my legs were stretched over his lap as he massaged my tired calves. I suddenly became very cold—as my teeth started to chatter and I felt hazy.

Dirk grabbed a thermometer. My temperature was 104 degrees. It seemed like I was looking through thick green glass with fog on the other side. Dirk called my doctor, the transplant clinic, and my parents. He insisted I go to the hospital.

At the hospital, I asked for hot blanket after hot blanket. The doctors and nurses wanted to get my temperature down so they did not accommodate my wishes. They started an IV and it felt like ice water was pumping through my veins.

I had a raging bladder infection despite the fact I did not have symptoms until the fever. After a few days of IV antibiotics the infection was under control and I was discharged.

It was in the emergency room that night that Dirk first met my mom and dad. They immediately knew he was a take-charge guy.

CHAPTER THIRTY-TWO

Dirk continued working on his Ph.D., and I was working on my M.B.A. in business and marketing management. He focused like a laser on completing his dissertation, and worked compulsively and feverishly without breaks.

He encouraged his other graduate school classmates to power through their dissertations as well. He would ask them, "Do you know what you call the person with the worst dissertation?"

"Doctor."

His singular focus on his dissertation, however, diluted his singular focus on me. I wondered if my time had come and gone as I became more and more discouraged about his lack of attention. I thought our story might be ending. The truth was, it was just beginning. Dirk was simply getting his ducks in a row.

After he thoroughly presented his Final Oral Examination to his dissertation committee, they unanimously recommended he was eligible to receive his doctoral degree and graduate. He was ecstatic. As he was leaving, they said three words that made all his hard work worthwhile, "Congratulations Dr. Miller."

I didn't realize I was the next duck. So I was flabbergasted when on Halloween night in 1993—the newly minted Dr. Dirk Miller asked me to marry him. We had never discussed marriage so his proposal caught me completely off guard.

It was a Saturday and we were both at our offices. He called me and asked if I would join him in St. Paul, and go get a bite to eat. Wearing an oversized green sweatshirt and black workout leggings—I hopped in my metallic cream colored Audi A4 and headed straight to St. Paul.

I had warned Dirk on the phone that I was dressed in workout clothes. No matter, he assured me. We had a sense of anticipation on the phone—we were both in a good mood and wanted to see each other. I knew a fun night was in store.

He took me to a cozy restaurant called Muffuletta, graced with simple wood tables covered in cream linens and bistro chairs.

In this quaint setting we shared a delicious dinner. My clock ticks at a slower speed than Dirks, so my eating pace did not match his race through the meal.

He seemed flustered and started to fidget in his seat.

"Are you done yet?"

"No."

"Be done already!" Put your cutlery down." He was quite insistent.

I was amused that we were actually bantering about my cutlery status. Finally, I was done and the waiter came and cleared my plate.

He soon returned with a flute of champagne followed with a dozen red roses. I looked at Dirk and saw a twinkle in his eyes, and a suppressed smile trying to form on his lips.

"Why did the waiter just bring me flowers and champagne?"

At that moment Dirk pulled out a huge plastic bracelet shaped like a diamond ring.

"Will you marry me?"

I sat there stunned. Was this a joke? The ring was a joke—so was this whole thing a joke? I felt like I had been knocked down and had to regain my equilibrium. I sat in stunned silence, staring like a deer caught in the headlights.

The twinkle in Dirk's eyes started to fade. I watched his face shift in slow motion from excitement to complete vulnerability.

"You are going to say yes, aren't you?" he said with slight panic in his tone.

My mind raced ahead as if on fast-forward. I thought of my health, "what would become of me—what kind of future was Dirk signing on for—would I be a drag of a wife—I can't believe he wants to stick it out with me—maybe I do have a future —he obviously is betting on it—that fake ring *better* be a joke—I worried I would never get married—now I am being asked—can I do this? Should I take the leap?"

Impulsively I answered the question bouncing around my mind— I will leap. Then I started to blurt out miscellaneous and random statements.

"We could have a dog!"

"We could have a house!"

"We could have a kid!"

I erased the fear from Dirk's face and said, "Yes, I will marry you."

CHAPTER THIRTY-THREE

We were engaged! I wanted to get married as soon as possible. My kidney transplant was three years old and my autoimmune disease was taking its toll on my new kidney. I didn't know how much longer I would have kidney function.

The prospect of future dialysis was always in my mind so I wanted to plan our wedding for the summer. We decided to save money, consolidate our apartments, and live in Dirk's (bigger) apartment in the months before we got married. Our apartments were side by side on Dean Parkway, so I moved into his building right next door.

I was surprisingly emotional about leaving my own space. It was my first independent apartment. I felt accomplished that I had a job, paid my own rent, had my own car, and made my life work despite some tough circumstances.

Dirk helped me pack. The time had come to say goodbye to the space that was my own so I could merge my life and space with Dirk. I looked long and hard at the charming apartment in its empty state.

The thin planked oak wood floors, the plaster archways that separated my television area from the dressing area and bedroom, the little bathroom with old hexagon tiles that never seemed clean (no matter how hard I scrubbed them), the Formica counters, and dull stainless steel sink in the tiny kitchen had all become so familiar.

I choked up as I felt I was losing a part of me—I was saying goodbye to my single self. Then I took on the excitement of saying hello to the next chapter in my life. My life with a future. My married life. My life shared with Dirk.

CHAPTER THIRTY-FOUR

Saturday, June 4, 1994

On a perfect sunny Minnesota day, Dirk and I were married.

We hired a string quartet that played Bach's "Jesu, Joy of Man's Desiring," Purcell's "Trumpet Tune," and my favorite traditional folk song, "The Ash Grove." I first heard this melody in my 6th grade choir class, and always thought it had a simple, sweet beauty.

I learned to play it on the piano. My mom heard it often as I repeatedly spilled these notes throughout our home when I was in junior high. When it was played at our wedding, I turned around, smiled at her, and winked.

I was living my own Kodak commercial moment.

Our reception was at the Wayzata Country Club, and it was spectacular. The food was served from buffet stations, and was delicious. The flowers were beautiful. The guests were celebratory. Dirk and I were delighted. The band was fabulous and played a variety of music that engaged all the age ranges of our guests.

Lisa and Rachael were my bridesmaids, Beth was my maid of honor, Dawn (who had since reunited and became engaged to Larry) was my personal attendant, and so many friends and family gathered with us to celebrate.

My dad and I danced to a modified "Brown Eyed Girl." He did

not fully realize it would be an up-tempo song, so shortly after we started dancing he looked slightly horrified and whispered "How long is this song!?"

Then Dirk and I danced slowly to "What a Wonderful World." The lyrics perfectly described how I felt as Dirk and I started our married life.

Two days after we were married we went on our honeymoon to the South of France. We started in St. Raphael, and stayed at a charming inn with a picture perfect pool surrounded by lush vegetation.

Arriving late in the day, we were shown to our room by a tall, dark, handsome French host. He allowed us to settle in, and then offered us a special meal in the dining room.

We enjoyed perfectly prepared salmon with an array of colorful and delicious fresh vegetables. It was incredible and we felt delighted to be launching our lives in this spectacular Mediterranean setting.

As we sat on the dining patio, we looked up and noticed the corner window to our bedroom, which was up a story-and-a-half level. A door from our room led to a balcony, and this was adjacent to another balcony that abutted another guest's room.

Tired from traveling and ready dive into the soft bed, we went up to our room and quickly fell asleep. I woke up in the middle of the night and had a strange sense that there was someone else there. Groggy and foggy, I was in the state between awake and asleep.

Abruptly, I sat up and saw a tall man out the glass door on the balcony. He was crouched down and looked menacing. He had on a black cap, and his beady eyes penetrated through the glass in the darkness.

Cloudy and confused, I nudged Dirk. "Dirk…wake up. Someone is watching us sleep."

Dirk bolted up and the creepy man jumped out of sight. Dirk ran to the balcony and found my unzipped purse. My credit cards and wallet were gone.

I quickly looked to my bedside where I had set my beautiful new wedding ring. It was custom designed after my grandmother's ring and combined all that was old and new. The gorgeous white diamond ring (surrounded by platinum filigree, small white diamonds, and rich blue sapphires) was gone.

Dirk's Rolex, wedding ring, wallet and credit cards were also gone. On the first night of our honeymoon we were robbed in the South of France. I felt sick.

Dirk ran into the hallway of the inn yelling, "Help, Help." No one came. We had to wait until morning, and did not sleep another wink that first night.

The next day we told some other guests at the inn what had happened. A nice man from Germany said he heard Dirk yelling in the middle of the night, but he thought he was saying "Hello, Hello. Hello?" This would certainly have been an odd thing to scream in the middle of the night.

Dirk shifted into his fix-it gear and we were off. We drove to Cannes and settled things with Visa. They issued new cards, cancelled the old, and took care of everything immediately. Back on track, we notified our insurance agent and just carried on with the rest of our trip.

We continued on to St. Jean Cap Ferrat, Monaco, Aix en Provence, and Paris. Despite the robbery, we had a wonderful trip and were excited to start the rest of our lives.

In September we bought our first house—an updated 1950's rambler in Golden Valley. We loved it. It was clean, fresh, and filled with natural light. I was delighted to be out of our dark "garden" apartment and have a place of our own.

We liked our new neighborhood and neighbors. To the north we had the Schnacks, to the south we had the Schnecks. We were three miles to downtown Minneapolis, still close to the city lakes, and a neighborhood park was two blocks away.

Although there was only about one mile between our new home and Westwood Lane—I had traveled a long way. Six years ago I was going in reverse, now I was moving forward. We landscaped, planted flowers, decorated, and happily settled in to our first home.

Dirk had since admitted that the first day we met was not the first time he had seen me. He confessed to a semi-stalking prior to our initial conversation.

Apparently, he saw me walking into the apartment parking garage and followed me. He watched me walk up to my pearl white Audi A4 and made a mental note, "cute girl, cute car." Since he was a car enthusiast, he liked my choice in German engineering.

After we were married, however, the transmission on my car required a costly repair. He then modified his first impression, "still a cute girl...the car, however...not so much."

CHAPTER THIRTY-FIVE

As our marriage grew stronger, my kidney function grew weaker. After just one year of marriage, my kidney was close to failure. I became thin and tired, but I plowed on through.

In June of 1995, we went to Dirk's hometown to celebrate his mom's 65th birthday. Although I was frail, I felt well while we were there and was excited to celebrate this important birthday with our family.

The week after we returned from Pennsylvania I started to rapidly accumulate water weight. After five years and three months, I knew the kidney had run its course and I called Dr. Brown.

"It's time—let's put you back on the transplant list—start dialysis and get you feeling better." Dr. Brown rung the bell and my second round of dialysis had commenced.

Soon afterwards, Dr. Brown said he had some big news. He was retiring. I felt shaken; I had mistakenly felt he was looped into this with me. I did not know kidney disease management without him. I felt happy for him—and selfishly, I also felt abandoned and jealous.

Dr. Brown's retirement amplified my sense of aloneness. If only I could retire from illness as easily as he could retire from nephrology. I knew I would find another nephrologist—and I knew this disease was mine and mine alone.

Dr. Somermeyer took over where Dr. Brown left off. My dialysis location changed and I went to Methodist hospital instead of Abbott. There had been some changes since I last was on dialysis, the significant one being that the run times had lengthened considerably.

Research indicated patients felt better and had fewer problems with longer dialysis treatments. So instead of my previous two-hour treatment, I started a three-and-a half hour dialysis procedure three times a week.

I would get to the dialysis unit after work, and sit in a chair for several hours. I passed the time by alternating between television and sleep. I routinely stopped at the nearby coffee shop in advance, bought a low fat lemon muffin, and savored it during the long boring dialysis run.

Each dialysis chair was situated within a pocket space, so the banter between patients was not the same as when Olga and I dialyzed together years before.

At this time, Dirk and I added a new addition to our household. We acquired a Wheaten Terrier puppy that looked like Mickey, and named her Zoe. She was the first new family member in our marriage.

This dialysis experience was easier to adjust to than my previous dialysis. This time, I did not have to experiment with harsh medications to try to alter the disease course. And because I had done this before, I knew I could do it again.

Before I was first diagnosed with focal sclerosis, I blindly traveled the path to eventual dialysis and transplant. It was like staring into a black hole. The second time around, my experience provided focus and added shape to the once ambiguous fear.

Clearly, this disease of focal sclerosis was a marathon, and I was strength training through repetition and resilience.

I was back to counting ounces, and restricting my potassium, sodium, and phosphorus intake. Yet all the balls were still in the air—working, dialyzing, and having fun with Dirk and little Zoe.

PART THREE

Let the sun shine.

CHAPTER THIRTY-SIX

November 30, 1995

I hustled down the hall to pick up the ringing phone. A doctor from the University was on the line and said, "Jennifer we have an excellent kidney for you—it is a five antigen match. It is close to perfect, can you come in and get it?"

"Of course" I said, suddenly feeling my knees buckle.

I screamed outside to Dirk as he was shoveling snow in the driveway, "Dirk they have a good kidney for me!"

He rushed in and instantly shifted into his highly focused gear. I could see it in the way he moved, on his face, in his look of determination. So soon and so scary. My mom and dad were out of the country in the Cayman Islands and everything was happening very fast.

It was a blur from this point on—Dirk handled it. He helped me pack a bag, he made all the appropriate calls, and he raced us to the hospital in record time. My mom and dad were trying to get on a flight home as soon as possible.

Nurses started prepping me and before I knew it I was in the OR waiting area with Dirk by my side. Dirk kept squeezing my hand as the anesthesiologist talked and put something in my IV to "relax" me. I felt it hit the vein. The next thing I remember is waking up.

A few days after the surgery, Dirk was with me in the poorly lit hospital room. It was overflowing with balloons that were sent from well-wishers (flowers were not allowed in the room for new transplant patients.) I was ready to take my first post-surgery shower and Dirk was there to help.

I had a fresh boomerang shaped incision on my lower stomach opposite my first transplant scar. Red and covered with steri-strips, the wound hurt and I was hunched over to ease the pain. My abdomen was distended, and my body was swollen from all the fluid they pumped into me.

As Dirk helped me into the shower, he looked at me as though I was the most beautiful woman in the world. His promise was tested...for better or worse. A+.

I spent five days and four nights in the hospital. Just like before, the machines buzzed, a blood pressure cuff squeezed my arm, scales rolled through the halls, and the endless sounds from the television provided white noise.

Minute by minute, my body was healing. My second wound was contained with stiches and staples and I knew like before, there was nothing I needed to do to direct the internal mending. Healing would simply happen.

I did need to adhere carefully, once again, to a regiment of anti-rejection medications. These medications are the single reason that a transplant recipient does not reject the organ. In essence, your body knows when tissue is not your own, so the natural body response is to get rid of the intrusion. The miraculous medications that suppress the immune system prevent the attack.

Some people find it daunting to require medication every day for the rest of your life (or for the lifespan of the kidney). I spoke with another transplant recipient who felt burdened by the daily responsibility. I found it helpful to think of all the other things I do daily—without burden. Brush my teeth, take a shower, brush my hair, eat, drink—surely if I can do these without a second thought, I can set up and take medications as part of my routine.

And, I knew this routine. Same dance, different dance floor. Yet there was a big difference from my first transplant—I did not have the sudden shift on the second day that indicated the protein leak was back. My urine output was strong and I was off to a good start.

We knew that recurrence of the focal glomerulosclerosis was likely, but so far so good. A doctor had told me years earlier that a transplant should be considered a vacation from dialysis. The possibility of dialysis always was part of my reality and would keep me alive if I had kidney failure. Transplants were not forever and they were not foolproof.

I was grateful he managed my expectations and I knew to appreciate every moment I had with my second kidney.

All the flowers that could not be received in the hospital were sent to our house. Several beautiful bouquets added fragrance and color to our home. I dried them, and used them to decorate our Christmas tree. It was a visible reminder of all the magic and love that surrounded us as we joyously celebrated the holidays with my second new kidney.

CHAPTER THIRTY-SEVEN

Things were going well, and then all of a sudden, I felt really exhausted. Dirk and I had planned to go to a party but I just couldn't muster the energy to get up. I was worried that there may be something going on with my kidney.

"I can't get off the couch Dirk. Really. I am so tired. Count me out...sorry."

"Wow Jenn, okay. I will go and stay for a little bit and be back soon. Enjoy the couch."

Something was going on with my body, but it was not kidney related. I did not realize at the time that a miracle was taking place inside of me.

The exhaustion continued. I was repulsed by various smells (oddly, I could smell asphalt driving down the road) skipped my period, and had sensitive breasts. Telltale signs. I stopped at a drug store and bought a pregnancy test.

I went into our bathroom and peed on the white stick. I waited. I looked. There it was—a little blue cross—positively pregnant. I walked down the hall of our rambler to tell Dirk as he watched football in the family room. He said he did not believe the test was accurate, ignored me, and continued to watch his game with interest.

Frustrated, I called my mom and she said, "You are not pregnant." Another skeptic.

Next I called Dawn, and she said, "If the test is positive you are pregnant." And so I was. Dirk and I became completely, undeniably pregnant. Unbelievable!

All the transplant literature I had read said pregnancy should wait until at least a year post-transplant. It had been seven months. My dad was terrified and told me not to tell many people. He feared I would have to tell them later that I was not pregnant. I refused to think this way.

Dirk said he did not want to be excited because something could go wrong. I rejected this thought process as well. "This is my one chance—my one moment" I explained. "If I will not be pregnant sometime in the future, if anything happens then—I can be excited NOW. Because NOW, at this very moment—regardless of what happens down the road, I AM PREGNANT!"

I could not contain my feelings of ecstasy and joy. I did it—I did it—I did it! I was beaming. I really wanted to have a baby. All my friends had babies and I wanted to have full membership in this club.

Just like life, pregnancy was black and white. I was not less pregnant because I had a kidney transplant. I decided to appreciate every pregnant day I had.

The secret of health for both the body and the mind is not to mourn the past or worry about the future, but to live in the present moment wisely and earnestly.

- Buddha -

CHAPTER THIRTY-EIGHT

July 1996

I experienced my first prenatal visit and met my remarkable OB/GYN, Dr. Virginia Lupo. She was very encouraging and explained her main concern was high blood pressure. She also said she was not sure where the baby would grow with all those extra organs in there (two transplanted kidneys in the front, one of which worked, and two native kidneys remaining in the back) but she was confident those organs would shift around to accommodate my little person.

I was already twelve weeks pregnant so my first trimester was over before I even knew it began. I read about the miracle of pregnancy and the week-by-week process of development. I had great confidence that eyes and limbs would form, limb buds would grow into hands and feet, the heart, lungs, brain, mouth, eyes, and spinal chord would develop perfectly.

Just like healing, I knew my body would take over and form a perfect baby. I used my creative visualization techniques and let the wonder take place inside of me.

The most thrilling part of the visit was the microphone that allowed me to hear my baby's heartbeat. My mom came with me to this visit, Dirk could not be there. I also had my first ultrasound and saw my baby—baby head, baby arms, baby legs. It was real.

September 2, 1996

I was 17 weeks pregnant and all was well. I just couldn't wait to be a mom. Since the previous Thanksgiving I had been on dialysis, received a nearly perfect transplant, and was now going to have a baby. This thought filled me with a profound sense of accomplishment and confidence that I could overcome any obstacles.

When I was 23 everything felt so bleak...so futureless. Now at 31, I somehow had the life I had visualized. Amazing husband, great job, good health, and baby on board!

I thought back to the evening Dirk proposed and smiled. We could have a dog! We could have a house! We could have a baby! Check one. Check two. Now...check three on the way.

September 14, 1996

Dirk and I went in for our 4-½ month ultrasound, and as I already knew, everything looked perfect and healthy. Dr. Lupo saw the baby's heart beating with four chambers, kidneys, hands, feet, smiling face and little moving mouth. She also saw that our baby was a little girl.

"Are you sure?" I asked Dr. Lupo with hesitation.

I knew a woman whose doctor told her the sex of her baby and said he had a 50/50 chance of being right. (No big revelation there.) I was hoping she was going for more accuracy.

"I can see that little hamburger bun perfectly," she said buoyantly, "You will have a girl without a doubt."

As I looked at Dirk he had tears in his eyes and his mouth

quivered. He admitted afterwards that he wanted a girl—and I confessed that I was praying for a sweet little girl as well.

I couldn't believe I was carrying my future daughter! I could only hope that I would be able to provide and experience the incredible closeness with her that I had with my mom. I had high hopes for our smiley, happy, full-of-life girl.

The name game soon began. Many names I liked were ruled out because Dirk had either dated a girl with that name or treated her for a mental illness.

Dirk wanted to name our daughter Zoe, which seemed ridiculous to me because our dog was named Zoe. He thought we could change our dog's name to Jo-Jo, but I rejected this idea.

I thought it would be too complicated to explain to the Schnecks and Schnacks, "Don't call Zoe Zoe because our daughter is Zoe so now Zoe is Jo-Jo."

We threw around Madeline, Angelica, Olivia, Liza, and Mackenzie. I called her Annabelle in utero until we could arrive at something. We also called her Little Cupcake, as Dr. Lupo always said during our visits, "The little cupcake is doing great!"

We both liked the name Liza the best—my mom's name is Elizabeth and Dirk had a great aunt named Eliza—so we chose Liza as a combination of the two family names. Liza Miller was on her way to the world.

CHAPTER THIRTY-NINE

I devoured books on pregnancy like *What to Expect When You Are Expecting,* and *What to Eat When You Are Expecting.* The second book discouraged the consumption of highly processed carbohydrates.

Always compliant, I strived to follow the book's recommendations without exception. As a result, I wasn't able to eat anything without fear. I called Steve and told him about the little known danger of eating bagels while pregnant. He laughed and said, "If your baby can handle your medications without a problem, I don't think a bagel is going to do much harm."

Then I called Lisa and before I expressed my concerns she said, "Whatever you do—don't read books on what to eat while you are pregnant. I know you will follow the advice too much and starve your child!" Bagels were back.

The pregnancy went well until I was 28 weeks along. I started to have recurrent bladder infections and an ultrasound showed that I had fluid backed up into my kidney.

Liza's growth caused a kink in my ureter, the tube that drains urine from the kidney to the bladder. This kink resulted in the backup of fluid called hydronephrosis.

I was hospitalized and told to take it easy for the remainder of the pregnancy. I was scared. Premature deliveries were common in transplant patient pregnancies and I wanted Liza to stay inside and develop until she was ready to be born.

While we were in the hospital, I confessed to a nurse that I was absolutely terrified. She asked me why and I explained that my baby was not due until February and I was at risk for premature delivery. I had not attended birthing classes yet.

"I don't know HOW to have the baby yet." I said with distress.

"Listen, women have been having babies in fields LONG before there were classes available. Jennifer, you will do just fine." she said with equal parts authority and compassion.

I took very good care of myself during the pregnancy by continuing to eat healthy foods and exercising on my parents' basement treadmill every day. A painting of an angelic woman hung on the wood paneled wall in front of the machine, and every time I exercised, I imagined angels orchestrating goodness for my baby girl.

After just over 30 weeks, something felt wrong. I rushed in to see Dr. Lupo and she said I had a premature rupture in the membrane sac that was holding Liza. I was slowly losing amniotic fluid.

She put me on bed rest immediately, and was concerned about infection risk and premature delivery. She scheduled an amniocentesis to determine if Liza's lungs were developed. As soon as the results indicated her lungs were ready, she thought the best thing for both of us would be to induce.

December 22, 1996

This was a tense day. The results of the amniocentesis from the week prior indicated Liza's lungs were still undeveloped. If she were born with lungs in this condition she would require a ventilator and face potential complications for survival.

Dr. Lupo did not know how much longer I could keep Liza inside with the loss of amniotic fluid. We had an amniocentesis in the afternoon to determine the condition of her lungs, and the results were critical.

I was far from calm. Two episodes of kidney failure and two kidney transplants were nothing compared to the fear that my baby may not be okay. I was as scared as I have ever been in my life.

We had the test done at HCMC and then went home to return to bed rest. Zoe rested by my side, and Dirk and I waited nervously for the call that would reveal if Liza's lung development would allow her to be induced the next day.

The call came. Good news—her lung development had increased significantly since the last week and she could be born without requiring ventilation. We knew we were going to have our baby girl within twenty-four hours!

CHAPTER FORTY

December 22, 1996

My nesting instincts took over completely. I couldn't stay on the couch anymore. I figured why be on bed rest when the next day was the predetermined birthday? I got up and cleaned and tidied in an attempt to have everything perfect in the house for the arrival of our baby.

Dirk and I had her bedroom set up with a new crib and bedding. We never painted the room, however, and I was really troubled that I didn't get this done.

I called my dad and Steve and asked them if they would come over and paint. They generously agreed and I picked my favorite pale pink color that relaxed me when I had acupuncture, and soothed me in my apartment with Beth. Their efforts transformed the room and all was ready.

Dirk and I went to bed early. We were expected at the hospital the next morning at 6:30 a.m. to start the induction. I woke up in the middle of the night to go to the bathroom. I had strong cramps and sat down on the edge of the tub to catch my breath.

The pains continued off and on through the night. In the morning, we gathered up our things and got in the car to go to the hospital. We had packed a CD player, and a stack of my favorite music. We were expecting a long day.

We had also prepared visualizations in advance to help me through the contractions. We loved our honeymoon, so we decided I should visualize being in the South of France as an escape from labor pains.

It was extremely cold and snowing heavily. I told Dirk my cramps were pretty strong and I got in the backseat to lie down.

Dirk was worried. I was obviously in pain as I was groaning in the backseat. Dirk raced through the empty, snowy streets at high speeds to get to Hennepin County Medical Center in record time. If he ever needs an alternate career, he is highly qualified for ambulance driving.

We arrived on time at 6:30 a.m. and I was wheeled up to the maternity floor. I was so happy to be there and felt safe knowing that I would be in good hands with the nurses and Dr. Lupo.

Several nurses came in and made me comfortable. As I was having contractions Dirk would hold my hand, as I just braced myself and managed to get through it.

When a contraction was over the pain subsided. The space between contractions was filled with conversations and excitement for our life ahead as parents. Then another contraction would come and we would move through it, knowing it would not last and we could handle it.

It occurred to me that these contractions resembled our life together. Kidney failure. Dialysis. Transplantation. Pregnancy. We endure the painful experiences and time passes. Other experiences are like the welcome rest in between that we embrace.

Dr. Lupo was not at the hospital yet, and the nurses were waiting for her to check and see how much I was dilated. The contractions were close together. With a concerned look my nurse asked me, "Jennifer, do you feel like you want to push?"

"Sort of," I said, not really knowing what it felt like to have a baby.

"We can't wait for Dr. Lupo. I need to check you now."

"When do I get the drugs for pain?" I asked as the nurse was checking to see how far along I was.

"You don't. You are dilated to 10—this baby is ready to be born. Get a doctor in here now!" she instructed to another nurse in the room.

Dirk looked at me and said, "You better pick your favorite song because I don't think we will be listening to an entire CD." I picked "More Than This" from the British band, Roxy Music.

A male doctor appeared and said he was going to assist me with the birth of Liza. Dirk looked upset. We didn't know this doctor from a man on the moon, and we really trusted Dr. Lupo.

"Where is Dr. Lupo?" Dirk asked. We were told she was on her way but the birth could not wait.

The male doctor sat down at the end of my bed and two nurses were instructing me how to breathe my way through the pushing. I was receiving on the job training.

The hypnotic song filled the room but failed to sooth me, as the contraction pain was stronger than any outside influence.

As we had planned, Dirk was trying to ease the pain by reminding me to visualize peaceful places. As the labor pain became very intense he encouraged me, "Go to the South of France, go to the South of France."

All I could do was focus inward on this experience of having my baby. I looked at him with wild eyes and snarled, "There is no way in hell I am going to the South of France!"

CHAPTER FORTY-ONE

Suddenly, Dr. Lupo ran in the room and said, "Let's have this baby!" The other doctor moved aside and Dirk and I were immensely relieved. We knew now, with Dr, Lupo in charge, it would be all right.

Liza was born. She popped right out, Dirk cut the chord, and Dr. Lupo placed her on my tummy. She was crying and coated with stuff and was the most beautiful little thing. What a wonder.

"She looks so big" I said. She was just over 4 pounds but it was the healthiest little 4-pound package I had ever laid my eyes on. A team of people whisked Liza away to the Neonatal Intensive Care Unit (NICU). Dirk went with them and I fell back into the pillows with a huge smile on my face.

I was oozing happiness. I couldn't believe I just gave birth to our little girl. Dr. Lupo had raced to the hospital in the snowstorm and didn't have time to do anything but run in the room and deliver Liza. "That is the first delivery I have ever done in my Eddie Bauer boots." she exclaimed.

It was 7:35 a.m. and we had been at the hospital for just about an hour. Liza was not induced, I did not have any medications for pain, and she was born naturally in record time at 33 weeks old.

My mom was planning on relieving Dirk later in the afternoon as we expected a long day of labor. I called her after Liza was born and said "I did it. I had the baby."

117

She was confused at first and thought she did not hear me right. Then she thought I was kidding, and she did not think it was a funny joke. Finally, she understood that I was serious and she said they were on their way.

In NICU, Liza was put in an incubator. She looked fragile and had feeding tubes, oxygen tubes, and heart monitors—yet she was so very beautiful.

I sang "The Ash Grove" to her constantly when I was pregnant. Now I was actually looking at her in the little enclosed incubator. I leaned over her little body and sang "The Ash Grove" softly. Her little head turned towards my song and me. "She knows me!" I thought. I was so happy to be her mom.

The doctors and nurses told us she would be in the hospital for about a week while she grew and became stable. A week went by and then they said it would be another week. And another week.

I felt really good and the 25 pounds I had gained during the 33-week pregnancy fell off. In 4 days I was back in my jeans—a little extra bonus.

My kidney function was tested. My creatinine was up and I was spilling protein. This was a concern to my nephrologist so they ordered an ultrasound. The pregnancy had furthered the hydronephrosis and more fluid was backed up in the kidney.

The fluid had to be drained to relieve pressure on the kidney. So while Liza was still in the NICU unit at HCMC, I went to the University Medical Center to get a percutaneous nephrostomy tube placed in my kidney.

The purpose of the tube was to drain the backed up urine and collect it in an external bag. The bag was to be attached with Velcro around my leg and hid under my pants.

It was supposed to be a fairly simple procedure performed in the

Radiology Department. I was given an oral antibiotic and a mild sedative right before the procedure. The tube was placed in my kidney and I went back to a hospital room while the medications that made me drowsy wore off.

Dirk came in afterwards and said, "How do you feel?"

"Not good" I said and suddenly started to throw up. Then with urgency, I had to get to the bathroom. As I jumped up to race to the bathroom I collapsed on the floor.

"NURSE!" Dirk yelled.

A nurse raced in and immediately saw I was in distress. She took my blood pressure and it was 55/30. Everything inside me felt like it wanted to come out. I could not get up and felt drained of my life force.

The urine that was backed up in my kidney was infected, and when the tube was placed the infection quickly spread throughout my bloodstream. I was septic.

This blood infection was suddenly poisoning me as the bacterial infection took control. I was put in ICU and flooded with antibiotics in an attempt to stop the infection, monitor my blood pressure, and keep my organs functioning.

It was very scary. My little tiny baby girl was at another hospital in NICU, and I was fighting for my life in a different hospital's ICU. It was the worst thing that could have happened and it came without warning.

Sepsis can kill people and I was determined to not be one of them. Thank goodness after days and days of massive antibiotic IVs I was stabilizing and moved out of ICU. Luckily, after several horrific days, I was cleared of the infection and able to go home.

CHAPTER FORTY-TWO

I wanted to see Liza desperately and was extremely emotional. A wonderful NICU nurse named Mary Ann was caring for her. I confessed to Dirk I was devastated that Liza was bonding with Mary Ann and would not love me.

He assured me, "Probably not likely that after you raise her she will tell people "I love my mom, but when I was 37 weeks old there was this special nurse...""

It was horrifying for Dirk when I was septic. He had a premature daughter in one hospital and a wife fighting for her life in another. He spent time between the two hospitals and worried what would happen if I did not make it. Was he going to be a new father without his wife?

"We are so lucky to have one beautiful daughter." Dirk said. "I am not going to go through this ever again." He then quickly scheduled a vasectomy and snip...our family of three was complete.

I was weak after I was discharged from the hospital and Mary Ann knew it. She noticed I could not stand for long during my visits with Liza. She knew I was not ready to have Liza home and she wanted me to wait one more week so I had more strength.

Finally, it was time to bring Liza home. Dirk and I were terrified because premature babies commonly suffer from apnea of prematurity and forget to breathe. In addition to their fragile lung development, their nervous system can be immature.

Interestingly, caffeine therapy helps premature babies breathe better. Liza was coming home with a heart monitor and we were required to give her doses of caffeine in her tiny bottles to control her breathing. After five eventful and difficult weeks in the NICU, she came home to her soft pink room. Zoe didn't seem phased by our new little bundle, and our life as parents began.

CHAPTER FORTY-THREE

Feed, sleep, and grow. That was the task for Liza's first several months at home. We kept careful watch on her breathing with the monitors, and were assigned a home health nurse that came and checked her weekly weight gain.

She made perfect progress. I loved her so much that I missed her when she was sleeping. I carried her often in a forward fitting sling so she could feel my comfort and warmth.

When I wasn't singing to her, I was talking to her. I had read that talking to newborns helps develop and increase their brain synapses, and I took that information to heart.

Babies are exhausting, however, and it took six months before she slept through the night. She had a bottle every three hours and Dirk and I took turns with the 1:00 a.m. and 4:00 a.m. feedings. It was easier for me because I would wake up, feed her in my arms on the loveseat in her room, and fall back asleep.

Dirk would wake up and stay up. Sleep deprivation made him a little crabby. He said he had to firmly squeeze his hand so he wouldn't nod off when he talked to his patients. As they talked about their issues he restrained himself from saying "You think you have problems? I have not slept for six months!"

Our pediatrician finally said Liza had put on enough weight so we did not have to feed her as frequently through the night. He explained it had become a routine for her, so it would be a difficult process to stop the feedings every three hours. He told us to expect her to cry, and explained the Ferber technique.

Basically, the Ferber method is a systematic program of letting your baby cry it out. It involves increasingly longer periods of time at night that you allow the baby to cry before you go in the room. Plus, when you do go in, you cannot touch or pick your baby up. In short, it feels like cruel and unusual punishment for both parents and babies.

But Ferberize we did. Liza's feeding time came. She cried. We heard. We waited. At first, we waited three minutes before we went in her room. Then five. The intervals increased, she kept crying. I wanted to cry too. Dirk wanted to sleep.

As the process continued, we were up to seventeen minutes. We looked at each other in the middle of the night, red eyes, painful expressions, and on the verge of breakdowns. It was heart breaking to hear her cry, and torturous to stop myself from going in to provide her with the simple comfort she craved. I did not know if I could do it anymore, it was just too hard.

"I can't take it." I told Dirk. "She thinks I am abandoning her—it feels so cruel." I started to get up.

And right then...she stopped. After seventeen minutes of crying on the fifth night, she stopped crying and slept through the night peacefully from that point on. Our Ferberization was complete!

It was a significant parent lesson in tough love, and our clue that raising a child was going to have its share of difficult moments.

All her physical milestones were slow due to her prematurity, but her cognitive development was right on track. Feed, sleep and grow she did. And before we knew it—our premature baby was sitting up, doing the army crawl, walking, talking, and constantly smiling and laughing.

She had an advanced vocabulary at a young age and was very talkative. I knew, of course, she was a genius (and credited her immense intelligence to all those brain synapses I developed with my diligently executed frequent-talking-and-singing program).

In addition to Liza, we called her Lizabella. As Dirk would say, "Her name is Liza. We call her Lizabella for long."

Suzanne was pregnant with her first child, and watched Liza two days a week when I would go to the office. I had known and loved Suzanne since kindergarten—no background check required. Her nurturing ways and tender nature made me feel calm as I left Liza for work.

Suzanne started called her Lizabella-Minella, and we sang to her "Lizabella-Bella-Minella doo doo doo doo doo doo doo" to the tune of La Cucaracha. Suzanne became Liza's Godmother.

When she was just over three, Liza started going to a preschool right by my office, called the Nutcracker Sweet. It was the right time for her to be around other kids and she thrived in the care of Debbie, Barbie, and Noni—three sisters who lovingly ran the preschool.

Liza's favorite lunch was a peanut butter and jelly sandwich, although I tried to shake it up every now and then. One day as I unpacked her lunchbox, I found her untouched roast beef sandwich along with a message she recited to Barbie "Mom, NO brown meat."

She flourished at preschool and formed very close bonds with the other kids and teachers. Her influences were expanding and she was soaking up a world beyond us. It was exciting to see her learn and develop into a little person.

I planted some tulips in the fall after Liza was born. The white and pink flowers were sweet so I called them my Liza tulips. They bloomed in the spring and were beautiful reminders of the wonder and beauty of renewed life. In the fall Dirk accidentally pulled them as he was getting the landscape tidy before winter. I was horrified.

Winter came and went, and the next spring arrived. Slowly but surely, as if untouched, those Liza tulips came back more full and beautiful then the year before.

CHAPTER FORTY-FOUR

Our home seemed a lot smaller once Liza became a toddler. It amazed me how one little being could claim so much space. I worked on many beautiful homes with clients and was rapidly collecting my own ideas. I also continued to look for building opportunities where Dirk and I could build our own custom home.

We were busy at L. Cramer, and my responsibilities continued to grow. I became the Vice President of Sales and Marketing, and worked with a steady stream of interesting clients on their special homes.

L. Cramer built rock climbing walls, basketball courts, gift-wrapping rooms, Tae Kwon Do rooms, indoor pools, and outdoor kitchens. My profession made it easy for me to dream, and dream big.

After a period of time, Dirk and I found a home site we liked. We bought it and started to design our new home. I poured all my energy into the plan.

Dirk encouraged me to take charge of the project as he continued to be very busy with the rapid growth of his eating disorder treatment program. We had named it The Emily Program after his sister, who had successfully recovered from anorexia and bulimia.

When Dirk and I first met, he had one employee…himself. At this point he had many more employees and was managing a complicated business.

When the construction project was underway, tensions flared between us. The stress of the building process intensified our other stresses. The combination simmered, and then bubbled up to a boil.

My kidney function was in decline as my creatinine kept steadily climbing. Liza was three and I was in a full mom-work-health juggle. Dirk was increasingly busy and our lives started to feel disconnected.

When we saw each other at night, we were both exhausted. One day would end, the next day would begin, and on our lives would go on. I started to feel like we were roommates.

Behind the curtain of our busy lives was an unspoken tension. When we sat together at night in our home, the air was thick with unspoken thoughts. Fears of our future. Fears of my health. Fear that we were losing the connection that brought us together.

As a result of my transplant medications I was dealing with side effects. Because the medications suppress the immune system, skin cancers are very common in transplant recipients.

I had frequent appointments with my dermatologist. Any indication of a skin lesion was biopsied to make sure it was not cancer. If the biopsy did show the lesion was skin cancer, it was quickly removed. Many of my biopsies showed squamous cell cancer.

If a squamous cell carcinoma is caught early and removed, it is unlikely to spread. If it is not caught early and spreads throughout the lymph nodes, it can be extremely serious. Because of this I was very careful to limit my sun and always wear sunscreen.

Dirk started to worry and became withdrawn. I felt lonely and resigned myself to the deeply buried dread that my health was too much for Dirk to handle. We both became entangled in our own force fields of withheld emotions, unspoken fears, and self-protection.

We knew we were at a crossroads, and we had to choose our direction. We grabbed onto the unspoken thoughts that clung in the air and articulated them. And an amazing thing happened. This simple process of authentic articulation freed us from the heavy weight we had placed upon our marriage.

We reevaluated why we were together, we regained our perspective, and we reconnected. We both appreciated we were in the exact place we wanted to be. We moved in to our newly built home and started to make memories there with Liza and Zoe.

CHAPTER FORTY-FIVE

Liza was a girly girl. She loved dolls and our home was sprinkled with Groovy Girls, Barbies, and American Girl dolls. Kit Kittredge was the first of her many American Girl dolls, and Liza and Kit became inseparable.

Each American Girl doll comes with a book that details the background of the character. Kit came with us everywhere and was a prominent member of the family—of course she was firmly held in Liza's arms in our Christmas card that year.

When people would comment to Liza that they liked her doll, Liza would recite word for word from her Kit biography, "Her name is Kit. She is a clever, resourceful girl that grew up during the Great Depression."

The following Christmas, Liza asked for a friend for Kit and so Josefina entered our lives. After she unwrapped Josefina, she burst with happiness and excitement. She got up and ran over to hug me— her arms flailing. As she ran to my outstretched arms, she swung her arm straight up and punched me in the eye. I had a black eye for weeks to remind us how much she loved Josefina.

Barbies were also her playmates and she imagined story lines for each one. She explained that one character was the dominant older sister, another was shy and insecure, another was exceedingly generous, and the mom was a firm enforcer of the family rules.

Dirk's brother Kim mused that Liza would someday create a one woman play in which she would write, direct, produce, and of course—be the star.

Our house was a whirlwind of dolls, crayons, markers, paints, a dollhouse, a little kitchen with fake food, dress up clothes, jewelry, sparkly tiaras, and lots of books. When Liza misplaced something, she would yell down the stairs to Dirk and me, "I can't find my pink Barbie dress."

"Where did you look?" I would yell back.

"Nooooooowhere...."

"She really needs to work on her looking skills." Dirk observed.

Despite her love of sparkly things (as she would leave kindergarten in a gold lame cowboy hat and pink heart shaped sunglasses her teacher would say "See you later Hollywood.") people often commented that young Liza had an old soul.

When my Grandmother died while Liza was very young, she wrote a poem about her death that moved my Uncle Bob to tears. I of course, cherished the many sweet notes and drawings that told us how much she loved us. I was happy that she knew she was loved as well.

One day she said to me, "Mom, if you had other children, would you feel so bad because you would love me more?" She was a funny, delightful, creative kid, and her character filled our house with joyful energy.

PART FOUR

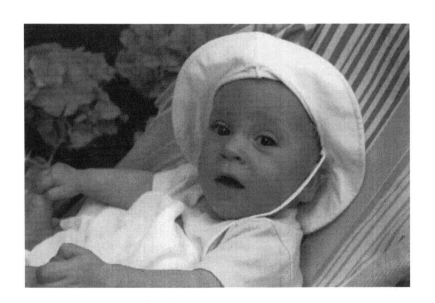

Jennifer Cramer-Miller

CHAPTER FORTY-SIX

I had an appointment at the University to evaluate my lab work, and my mom joined me. I saw Dr. Gildner, an accomplished surgeon with an Austrian accent, silver-blue eyes, and a clear concern for his patients.

We met in a small clinic room as my mom waited for me in the lobby area outside. My creatinine was quite elevated. Matter-of-factly, he said, "You need another transplant. We need to find you a living donor. Who is here with you?"

"My mom" I said.

"She could be your donor. Let's have her tested."

I knew my kidney function was declining, but I did not expect these words. I walked out of the room and sat down next to my mom in the waiting room.

"What did he say?" she asked.

"He said I need another transplant, and he said you should get tested."

"What?" she asked in confusion.

"I know…kinda crazy."

"Can I?" she wondered. "I thought I wasn't a match before."

"Apparently there are some developments in antibody matching so they can test you again." Although I was saying these words with my mouth, my mind did not embrace or comprehend what this meant. It was quite a shock.

133

Kidney matching refers to the compatibility of a donor to the recipient. The first criteria is blood type matching. The four major blood types are A, B, AB, and O. My mom and I both have blood type A.

Tissue typing is another factor, and it was weighted more heavily in years past than it was in 2002. There are six HLA antigens (human leukocyte antigens) that were previously thought important to match for kidney transplant compatibility.

Possibly due to improvements in anti-rejection medications, research suggested that there was not a statistical difference in success between one-antigen matches and five-antigen matches. Therefore, this measurement became less important over the years since my first transplant.

"Well let's check into it," my mom said, as if this was just another riot.

I was not surprised at her generosity. It was just a shining example of the generosity she had always shown me for 37 years. Yet this was on a grand scale and I was overwhelmed.

I had reservations…of course. What if she had major surgery to remove her kidney and I rejected it? What if the kidney did not work? What if it failed soon after I received it? What if she has complications with the surgery? My kidney problems have already been enough of a burden for her. So many fears. So many doubts.

I started expressing these to my mom and she looked at me squarely in the eye and said "Would you do this for Liza?" Before I could answer out loud she locked her eyes with mine and said "I am doing this…don't say another word."

It is impossible to accurately articulate my gratitude for my mom. She has always seen the shine in me, and loved me without conditions. She has always been a steady force of judgment-free love and acceptance. If there is ever a mold made for the model of the perfect mom, it should be based on mine.

She has played with me, fed me, tucked me in, read books to me, made crafts with me, volunteered at my school, set out after school snacks for me (Hostess Ho-Hos no less) been silly with me, set limits when I was a teenager that I thought were attempts to ruin my life, lived her own life, showed me a mom could have her own interests, friends, and social life, made me laugh, cared about me when I was sad, was happy for me when I was glad, loved me for who I was and who I am.

And that would seem to be more than enough, yet, at the age of 65, with her characteristic grace and unconditional love; she offered to undergo surgery to give me her kidney.

She was doing what moms do—she wanted to shield me from harm and protect me. Now that I was a mom, I had a profound awareness of this formidable instinct.

From the very start, it kicks in—the nap time is ferociously protected, the car seat is fastened tight and just right, the food is healthy, no pesticides and no nasty hormones, bedtime is critical, television is monitored, fresh air, ample play time—it all factors into the fierce predisposition of a Momma Bear.

When Liza was about three or four we were at a park with some of her friends. She came up to me; her big brown eyes tinged with fear, and said there was a scary boy saying mean things to them.

This boy was quite a bit older than they were. "Go talk to him Mom, go talk to him!" she pleaded with big eyes.

I went over and told him he was saying things that were upsetting the younger kids and I kindly asked him to stop. He may have felt like a big shot when he was talking to three and four year olds, but he shrunk when I talked to him. He looked at me like I was a super scary park lady.

As I walked away from him, Liza ran up to me and threw her arms around my legs. She was bursting with relief that I "saved" them from harm. She felt safe within the boundaries of my fortress.

Likewise, my mom was doing what she could to wrap her bubble of protection around me. But her gesture was far beyond talking to a kid in the park, she was confronting my bully by giving up her kidney.

CHAPTER FORTY-SEVEN

We proceeded with the testing. The preliminary blood tests were done and I did not have antibodies that would cause me to reject her kidney. The next steps involved many tests for my mom to see if she was suitable for surgery.

She had a preliminary physical and blood pressure screening. From there she had a series of lab work, x-rays, and an EKG to determine the health of her kidneys, liver, heart and lungs. Aids and hepatitis tests were also done, as well as tests to see if she had been exposed to viral illnesses. Urine tests and psychosocial evaluations rounded out the workup.

I originally had doubts about getting multiple transplants knowing the lifespan of my transplants was limited. Yet, various nephrologists told me that the average lifespan of a kidney transplant without focal sclerosis was only a few years longer than my transplant lifespans.

Transplantation is typically cost-effective in comparison to alternate dialysis costs that would be necessary without the transplant. Medicare covers the majority of costs for both dialysis and transplantation, and I have been fortunate to also have additional supplemental insurance coverage.

It was a relief to hear the cost/benefit analysis was favorable, because far from economics—this was emotional. I was motivated to live a productive life with a kidney.

My mom was 65 years old and in good shape. After the extensive review, the team of doctors cleared her to be my kidney donor. Dirk, Mom, Dad, and I met with Dr. Matthews at the University to ask questions and express concerns.

"Is a 65 year old kidney good enough?" my mom asked.

"We know 65 year old kidneys have less function than younger kidneys." explained Dr. Matthews. "But Jennifer will be much better off to receive your kidney now than if she were to wait five years on a list while she was on dialysis."

There is a shortage of available kidneys, so the wait can be considerable. A five-year wait is not uncommon, and it can be quite a bit longer for some recipients. Dialysis is a wonderful kidney replacement alternative that keeps people alive. A successful transplant, however, if possible, is a more desirable option for many.

My mom's offer eliminated the stress of a waiting period and allowed me to avoid dialysis. We also were able to plan for the surgery and schedule a time that worked for both of us. It was an awe-inspiring gift, and I felt miles beyond fortunate.

Dr. Matthews detailed the risks of the surgery and explained it was a relatively safe and reasonable choice for my mom and me. We discussed it, decided to go forward, and set the date to be July 11, 2002.

This was the day my mom intended to have major surgery and give me life, again. This was to be the date of my third transplant.

My mom's original birth name was Mildred Elizabeth McNulty, but since she was never fond of the name Mildred, she went by Elizabeth and Liz for most of her life. When she gave me her kidney, she named her gift Milly because she was giving me a part of herself.

CHAPTER FORTY-EIGHT

The surgeries were performed one after the other. In one OR they removed my mom's kidney, and in the next OR they transplanted it into me.

Slightly delusional, I convinced myself it would be fun being in the hospital together. It really wasn't much fun. Of course we both were in pain, and fairly groggy from the medications.

Our rooms were on different floors. When I was feeling a little better on day two, I was wheeled up to my mom's room to see her. She was being given morphine for pain, and her speech was slurred. I felt terrible when I saw her.

I hated that she was in that dull blue hospital gown with IV tubes and a painful expression on her face—knowing it was because of me. I prayed for her get better so we would know we made the right choice.

She did get better. It was a slower recovery for her but after a few weeks she was well on her way. Dirk would drop me off at her house in the morning and we spent time improving together. Soon our bodies healed and our lives seemed to be restored to "normal."

Life changes are frequently referred to as the "new normal." I was going for the "new-new-new normal." Three times the charm?

I had healthy lab values and my mom had given me more time to enjoy life without the imminent threat once again of dialysis and kidney failure.

Liza wrote a paper for her English class titled *A Mother's Love*, and her introduction so eloquently described my feelings for my mom as well.

"I believe in a mother's love. The love that delivers wings and sails you around the earth. The love that has seen you make a million mistakes and still believes in your perfection."

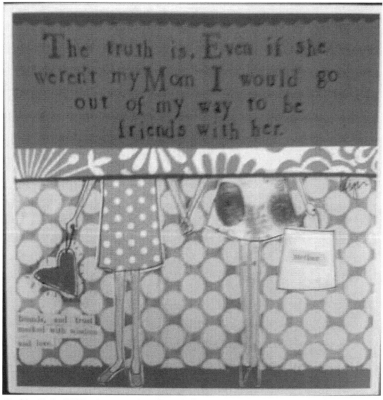

Card by Curly Girl Design artwork and words ©2008 Leigh Standly Publishing ©Curly Girl Design Inc/Leigh Standly

CHAPTER FORTY-NINE

With renewed health from Milly, life marched happily on. At work, I was enjoying the variety of fascinating clients and the lives in which I became professionally intertwined. One prospective L. Cramer client came from a family with great wealth. He inquired about building a home on his family's compound, close to the main family estate.

He explained there was a cook that prepared meals in the main house, and she would be cooking for him as well. In earnest, he asked us if we thought he should include a kitchen in his new home for resale.

Another client shared his secret desire to be a drummer. So to indulge his fantasy, he requested a stage with electric retractable curtains. He planned to have the curtains open dramatically, so with great fanfare he could stage a drum solo for his children.

We also built a room so half of a NASCAR racing vehicle could be placed in front of a large screen. The Owner planned to play a racing game on the big screen while sitting in his authentic car.

Although we certainly did not have any features quite as noteworthy, Dirk, Liza and I were content in our Overlook house. After five years, the itch to build another house led me to look for other lot opportunities.

L. Cramer was building in a neighborhood approximately five

miles west of our Overlook home. These sites were close to the charming shops and restaurants of Wayzata, and close to Lake Minnetonka.

So in a whirlwind, I put our Overlook house on the market and we bought a new lot. Our home sold in two days. Suddenly we needed to find a place to live as we built our new home.

When we packed up all our belongings into hundreds of boxes and moved out of our Overlook house, I thought about what makes up the place we call home. Is it the walls that contain us? Is it our things?

It seemed clear, as I explained to Liza when we moved into a small apartment as our new home was being built, our home is the place we are all together—and it is true that the best things in life are not things.

We rented an apartment near Lake Calhoun, very close to the apartment Dirk and I lived in before we got married.

It was a fun change of pace with the health club facilities, indoor pool, attached restaurants, and Lake Calhoun's biking trails, beaches, and walking paths.

It was tight quarters, however, and we did miss our space. To our complete surprise, Liza announced she did not want to have a television at the apartment. Dirk and I scratched our heads—we did not know where this idea came from. Yet she was insistent that it would be better for her if she did not have a television.

We wanted a television of course, but felt if the kid was begging to get rid of it…what's up with that? So we compromised and brought a television for our bedroom only.

It didn't take long before Liza let go of her self-imposed ban, so the three of us plopped in our bed watching TV. When Liza had her friends over they would also pile in our bed to watch an occasional

Disney channel show. Dirk retreated to the Beach Club restaurant with his terrible towel to cheer for his beloved Steelers.

There were other space shortage issues. Liza was taking piano lessons but we did not have room to bring our piano to the apartment. Instead, we had a small keyboard that she used for practice.

Her piano teacher was stern and scolded her for not practicing on a real piano. As her recital approached, her teacher's words replayed in Liza's mind and she became concerned about her upcoming performance.

I told her not to worry, I would make sure she had some pre-recital practice on a real piano. I had a plan.

"What are we doing here?" she asked reluctantly as we parked in front of Schmidt Music.

I whispered as though we were on a covert mission, "Pick a piano in the back and play. I will cover and talk to a salesman for as long as I can. Just keep practicing." I motioned to the back of the room with my head and set forth to execute Operation Practice.

I gathered many facts and figures about the baby grand piano options (I really would like one some day) as Liza skillfully pounded out Beethoven's "Fur Elise." When she felt sufficiently ready, we said goodbye to the helpful salesman and were on our way.

Needless to say, she did well at her recital, and we all looked forward to moving into our new home.

CHAPTER FIFTY

It was hard for Zoe when we lived at the apartment. She no longer had her yard for exercise, but she seemed to be losing weight. She was not as vibrant and was having frequent accidents.

One day Liza's friend Franny was over and the three of us went for a walk with Zoe across the street to Lake Calhoun. As Liza and Franny were playing in the park, Zoe was sniffing all the park smells.

Suddenly she toppled over. I thought she tripped, and said "Get up silly Zoe." She could not get up.

A woman came over and said, "I saw your dog go down, can I help you—I work with animals."

"I don't know what happened." I said confused.

She crouched down, listened to Zoe's breathing and felt for her heartbeat. "Your dog is in distress, you need to get her to a Vet right away."

I was really scared as I looked at poor Zoe helplessly lying there in the grass. Liza ran over with Franny and I quickly dialed Dirk in the apartment. "I need help! Zoe collapsed and we need to take her to the Vet" I said frantically.

Dirk ran out of the apartment, crossed the street to the park, and lifted Zoe in his arms. He urgently carried her across the street and turned back to say, "Take your car and meet me."

Liza and I dropped Franny at her home nearby, and proceeded to the Emergency Animal Hospital. As I raced into the parking lot, I saw Dirk coming out the hospital door. His face was sad.

The minute I looked at him I let out a gasp and started to cry.

"What?" Liza said, scared at my emotional outburst.

"I don't like his look, I don't like the look on his face." I blurted through tears and rolled down my window.

"She is dying." Dirk said. "The Vet said her heart is trying to stop and we could try to revive her but she is shutting down."

We all went inside the hospital and Zoe had died. Just like that, Zoe was no longer with us. I wanted to see her and say goodbye. Crying as I was led back to the room, I saw her on her side. She looked like she was sleeping. I hugged her body and told her what a great dog she was.

We had her cremated and were given a box with her ashes. All the time that we had spent with Zoe replayed in my mind and I cried for two days. Zoe entered our lives as an adorable puppy when we lived in our Golden Valley house before Liza was born.

Liza had never known life without Zoe. Her death marked the past eleven years—my 1995 transplant, Liza's birth, all the things we had experienced. I felt a deep loss for the passing of time and the cruelty of death.

It was like that *Marley And Me* moment where you have a flashback and think, "Where has all the time gone?" and then, "Where is it going?" and then, "Did we love her enough when she was here?"

Liza was very sad, and very wise. She tried to comfort me; my third grader gave me calming talks about the "circle of life." I marveled at her maturity about death, and her attempt to understand and articulate it. She wrote a poem for her third grade class and she was asked to read it at the assembly in the school Chapel.

Her third grade teacher emailed and said the third graders seemed quiet afterwards, and their teachers asked them what was on their mind. Apparently Liza's words touched them, so they had subsequent class discussions about what it means to love a pet, and how hard it is to lose things you love.

Zoe and Me
by Liza Miller, 3rd grade

Dedicated to my faithful dog Zoe (1994-2006)

A wheaten baby when they got her. Soft coated wheaten terrier with the cutest eyes imaginable. She was a playful pup. But that's just me.

Chapter 1. What I feel:

I don't feel much anymore since the accident happened almost three weeks ago. But when I see that box holding her ashes it brings me back to that dreadful day. And then I feel sorrow and a bit of anger. I don't know why. It just comes with the packet of my emotions. And then I remember her body lying helpless on the parks ground. And my Daddy carrying her body bundled in his arms like a squishy blanket. And then I think: No more Zoe. And then I think: No more yelling, "Come here Zoe" and clapping your hands. And then I think: No more pee to clean up and no more walks. And then I think: No more of my best friend.

Chapter 2. A simple house life:

It was hard enough to get her to "sit" and "shake" and "lie down" but we never did teach her not to jump on people. We always took that was a sign that

146

she had got to be the friendliest dog on the planet. Even though she was almost eleven I called her "My little puppy" cause in some ways she was a little puppy. So playful and energetic. But all there is in our house now is dead silence.

Chapter 3. Deep in my heart:

Zoe was as good as a sister to me. She meant so much to me. I loved her so much.

Zoe had physically left us forever and her death stabbed us with loss. The pain was sharp not only because she was no longer here, but because it emphasized the inescapability of death.

Can it be true that just like Zoe, we will all die one day—we will just vanish from what we now know? Even though we absolutely understand this is true, it is so hard to accept it. Our time together is limited and precious, so while we have life, our best choice is to live it.

CHAPTER FIFTY-ONE

In November of 2006 our new home was complete.

We hosted more birthday parties, holiday gatherings, fundraisers for The Emily Program Foundation, gatherings with friends and family, and slumber parties for Liza and her friends. Our lives unfolded within a new set of rooms and spaces on a new street in a different neighborhood.

Many hospitalizations and medical roller coaster rides emphasized our thankfulness for normalcies. Mundane activities were more than welcome in our home, and Dirk and I relished the rhythm of everyday.

I prepared the meals; Dirk cleaned up; I took Liza to school; Dirk got the morning coffee ready to go; I bought the groceries; Dirk checked the mail; I broiled; Dirk grilled.

Dirk's travel schedule increased as he networked with several other eating disorder programs in the United States and evaluated opportunities for Emily Program partnerships out of state. His staff had grown to over 150 people.

Although we missed Dirk when he was gone, Liza and I adjusted to having our own special time when he traveled. We shopped for lotions and make-up at Sephora, worked on homework, watched movies, and had our favorite spinach/cranberry/walnut salad for dinner with grilled salmon.

One evening we went to the mall and browsed around in Brookstone. Of all the useful products—I just couldn't resist purchasing a motorized grill brush. I imagined how easy it would be to clean the grill after our salmon was prepared.

When Dirk came home he scratched his head, visibly doubting the usefulness of my motorized grill brush purchase. I enthusiastically explained to him the value of such a handy tool. Unconvinced, he said he was going to get the mail.

"Good—I haven't gotten it since you've been gone."

On his way out I heard him mutter, "A motorized mail fetcher, now *that* would be useful."

Liza and I missed Zoe and talked about getting another dog, but Dirk was not sure he wanted to have a dog. He cited the work involved, the cost, the responsibility. We did not believe these were reasonable obstacles to loving a dog, and we persisted.

When Dirk was away on another business trip, Liza and I spent an evening researching various breeds. We came across really cute pictures of black and white fluffy dogs and discovered they were Tibetan Terriers. After reading about their temperament, we were intrigued. I expanded our online search to see if there were any local Tibetan Terrier breeders.

I was led to a local breeder's website, and realized it was Zoe's breeder! Now, in addition to Wheaten Terriers, Zoe's breeder, Earl Miller, bred Tibetans Terriers. I thought this must surely be a sign, so I called him.

Earl's partner Marc answered, and he explained the differences between the two breeds. "We have some Tibetan puppies right now, and there is one left. He is a little guy and we call him Flash. You should come and meet him."

"My husband is out of town so I should probably wait." I

explained.

"You don't have to do anything but meet him. Your daughter would have fun seeing the puppies, just come over and play."

Of course, he knew exactly what he was doing, and off we went. We drove to Marc and Earl's home and when we got there, Marc opened the door and the most adorable black and white puppy came bounding out—jumped on Liza, and showered her with sweet puppy kisses.

She fell in love at first sight. I fell in love at first sight. We left with an ache and a strong conviction that we just met the dog that was destined to be ours. Liza called Dirk on his cell phone and told him about little Flash. "Please Dad! PLEASE! I already love him!"

When Dirk arrived back in town we all went back to see Flash. Dirk felt he did not have a choice and agreed (very reluctantly) that we could bring little Flash home.

Liza was so happy as she held Flash in her lap as we drove home. I was excited. Dirk was silent. Liza decided to rename him, and chose the name Timmy. Timmy the Tibetan Terrier was the new member of our family.

CHAPTER FIFTY-TWO

I continued to have frequent bladder infections and was treated by Dr. Joanne Young to keep them at bay. I also struggled with a low hemoglobin as my kidney function slowly declined.

Setbacks came and went, but I paraded on with my good life. My transplant coordinator, Mary, used to tease me about my determination to live with my transplants in the background, as opposed to front and center.

When she tried to schedule my follow up appointments, I would tell her I had to wait and see if I had a client meeting at that time. "Jeez Jennifer—don't let a little thing like a kidney transplant interfere with your schedule."

My high school friends and I made it a priority to carve out friendship time, so we planned annual winter get-aways. We typically went to sunny spots where we could all be together with pools, spas, good restaurants, cocktails and conversations.

We had been to California and Arizona, and decided to change it up with a long weekend in Las Vegas. The six of us stayed at the Bellagio and had a wonderful time. Beth, Suzanne, Amy and I were the Minnesota girls. Liz came from Telluride, Carrie traveled from Los Angeles, and Racheal flew from Milwaukee.

Rachael emailed each of us in advance suggesting that since Las Vegas was a crazy place, we should be crazy too. She insisted we all bring a wig to wear out one night on the town.

The last time I bought a wig was not a laughing matter. This wig experience was all about fun. So with giddiness, we pursued our plan.

Liz and I became pageboy redheads, and we were respectively named Roxy and Adelaide. Rachael and Beth became longhaired brunettes. Amy replaced her straight blonde hair with a Dolly Parton doo, and Suzanne rocked a spiky brown number we called the "Rod Stewart."

Carrie could not bring herself to stoop to this level of humiliation. Her husband jokingly told her as she left Los Angeles, "A gigolo would be okay, a wig…out of the question."

We ordered champagne in the room before we ventured out wearing our synthetic atrocities. As we walked off the elevator Carrie pronounced our status, "Walking into lobby…we are walking into lobby," as if she were an undercover agent keeping us focused on our mission.

We stood by the Bellagio slot machines and asked an older couple if they would take our picture. The woman gladly snapped a few shots. Rachael asked if she would like us to take a picture of her with her husband, and she said "Oh no…we don't do pictures," flashed us a mischievous wink and continued, "He is not my husband." Apparently, things were happening in Vegas…

That night at dinner we each set goals to achieve within the year before our next annual trip. My goal was simple; I did not want to be on dialysis next year. I wanted my mom's kidney to be working in a year, and I wanted it with all my being.

The following year we went to The Parker in Palm Springs and had another fabulous time together. And yes, Milly was still working. I had less function than the year before—but I had function—and was so happy to be vacationing with my friends, once again, without the need of a machine to cleanse my blood.

CHAPTER FIFTY-THREE

My mom and dad were married on December 26th in 1959. As the Christmas holiday approached in 2009, so did their 50th anniversary. We all wanted to celebrate their remarkable 50 years together, and planned a large party with family and friends.

The party was at our home and was a perfect event. Steve flew in from New York and told us he had met a special woman and their relationship was serious. His girlfriend, Merly, lived in Cartagena, Columbia and she could not yet travel out of the country. Other than Merly, everyone was there—aunts, uncles, cousins, nieces, nephews, and dear friends.

Steve and I gave toasts to our mom and dad, and felt fortunate to be gathered with so many people that loved our parents. I felt happy and lucky to be able to host the event at our house.

I also knew my remaining kidney function was slim. My legs and ankles felt tight from swelling. I tried to hide the fear that Milly's run was almost over, but deep down I knew it was a matter of time.

In January, my labs showed the continued elevation of my creatinine, yet I told my doctor I was not ready go on dialysis again.

We had determined that I would not get another transplant right away, and that a period of time on dialysis would allow my body to take a break from the side effects of anti-rejection medications.

Our annual girlfriend trip had been planned for early February in Cabo, Mexico. I was determined to go. Dr. Davin was monitoring my lab work and encouraging the start of dialysis. I continued to insist that I wanted to wait.

I felt emotional about losing my mom's kidney. This was my mom's gift—I wanted it to be with me always. Although I always knew it would come to an end, it was very hard for me to accept.

I told my mom how bad I felt about losing Milly. She was very matter of fact about it. "We should be happy about all the good years Milly provided, we knew it wasn't going to be forever."

I knew she was right, but I still felt a strong feeling of defeat and loss. Cabo was approaching and I desperately wanted to make it on this trip with my friends. I bought a ticket, looked forward to it, and crossed my fingers.

I saw Dr. Davin again and he checked my labs. We discussed my plans to go to Cabo. He strongly discouraged it and said it would be dangerous for me to travel with such minimal kidney function. His typically light-hearted tone was serious, and I had to accept his words. I knew he was right. I had a terrible metallic taste in my mouth—a classic sign of kidney failure.

He admitted me to Abbott Hospital to start dialysis treatments as an inpatient. He wanted me to have three consecutive treatments to be sure I was stabilized before I was to start three times a week at an outpatient clinic.

Dirk called Delta Airlines. The plane ticket to Cabo was refunded. I started dialysis. My friends flew to Mexico. I was devastated. It was February 2010.

PART FIVE

Fall down seven times. Stand up eight.
- Japanese Proverb-

Live Happy (...damn it)

CHAPTER FIFTY-FOUR

D r. Davin encouraged me to think about learning to do my dialysis treatments at home. He thought I was a perfect candidate and wanted me to give it some thought. I was reluctant—I thought there might be some advantage to going to a clinic three times a week, come home, and separate my medical life from my "real" life.

I soon learned dialysis had changed quite a bit since my first two experiences at Abbott and Methodist hospitals. Since 1995, fewer hospitals provided outpatient dialysis services. Large companies like DaVita and Fresenius Medical Care became the main providers of dialysis services in the United States.

Unsure of the home dialysis option, I chose to go to a large outpatient clinic fairly close to my home. After three dialysis runs there I questioned my decision.

It was depressing and impersonal. Different technicians put in my needles and managed the machines each time, and some inspired more confidence than others.

On my third run at this clinic I had a technician set up my fluid pull rate and it was aggressive. It was supposed to be a slower ultrafiltration rate since I was new (again) to dialysis treatments and would need some time to acclimate.

As the machine filters the blood it pulls out toxins and fluids. If the machine is set to remove fluid too quickly, a significant drop in blood pressure can occur suddenly.

A blood pressure cuff encircled my arm and recorded my pressure every thirty minutes to ensure it was stable. If it dropped, an alarm would sound so a technician could adjust the machine.

My blood pressure felt low and I tried to get the attention of a nurse or technician. My mom sat with me and I told her I felt dizzy and light headed. She summoned a technician.

"She needs help!"

The technician came and discovered my blood pressure had dropped. She reclined me in my chair and slowed down the machine. After a few minutes I started feeling better. The technician came over again and said, "You seem okay, let's bump you back up."

Very soon after, I started crashing again. My mom screamed for someone to come. It was busy and loud, so it was difficult to get a technician's attention.

The charge nurse came over and quickly shut down the machine rate and pushed my chair as far back as it would go. I was wiggling my feet in an attempt to stay with the world. I felt like I was close to passing out and slipping away.

She asked me how many dialysis runs I had so far at the clinic. I told her this was my third. As she looked at the machine settings she said under her breath, "Who would have set your machine at this high fluid pull rate. This is crazy." She shook her head in disbelief.

After some time I started to feel somewhat better, and my mom and I left. It was so helpful she was by my side because it would have been difficult to drive myself home. My Avocado, once again, to the rescue.

I decided I never wanted to go back there. It was too hard to feel safe when different people created such different outcomes. The next day I called Dr. Davin and told him I wanted to set up an appointment to get training for home dialysis. I wanted to be in charge of my own health care, and be my own technician. He thought I was making a good decision.

Dirk did too—in fact, he was pumped about it. He really believed together we could do this and it was the right approach. So we went to a Davita Home Dialysis office in downtown Minneapolis and met with Mary Gilbert.

I liked her right away, the staff was friendly, and the small facility was warm. It did not feel sterile like the outpatient clinic with its sticky gray vinyl floors and dimly lit space. It was clean and welcoming with warm caramel toned walls and a rich wood floor.

We saw two patients in leather-like reclining chairs that were dialyzing with the assistance of two attentive technicians, Mark and Lisa. It was small, quiet, and comfortable—the exact opposite of the outpatient clinic I had been to the day before.

Mary took us into her side office and told us about the program. She explained that we would learn how to operate the dialysis machine as I would get my dialysis treatments. I would come five days a week, and training would be complete in approximately three to four weeks. Then we would be able to have a machine at home and do our own treatments.

Fueled by my intense desire to be done with the outpatient clinics, I liked what I heard. Dirk did too. Mary asked us to start the following week and be there at 8:30 on Monday morning.

Dirk notified his office that he would not be available for meetings until after 1:00 for the next month. I notified my office as well, and our home dialysis training began.

CHAPTER FIFTY-FIVE

We learned how to prepare and monitor the machine, manage the inventory, track my blood pressure, pulse, and temperature, keep records of the run, clean the equipment, order supplies, make SAKS, replace PAKS, and deal with various alarms.

I also learned how to insert the large needles in my fistula so that my blood could be pumped into the machine and be cleaned. Once the artificial kidney cleaned my blood, it was returned through the second needle line.

Once again, my diet was limited on fluids, phosphorus, salt, and potassium. I also required shots of Epogen to help with extreme anemia. Epogen stimulates the production of red blood cells and is the same drug that Lance Armstrong used illegally to enhance his performance. I had not planned to compete in the next Tour de France or Olympics, so a doping scandal was not on my list of concerns.

After our dialysis training was complete—the machine was delivered to our home. We set it up in our bedroom niche by the windows.

The plan was to give myself dialysis treatments five to six days a week for two hours. Frequent runs were to reduce the blood chemistry highs and lows from my kidney failure. My restrictions would be less severe and my energy would be more stable. Plus, I could set my own schedule, an extremely appealing bonus.

I had been on dialysis before so I thought I knew what to expect. I imagined I would go to work, sit down at night for a couple of hours, watch television, and clean my blood.

It was not as easy as I had imagined. At first, it was beyond overwhelming. I hardly recognized myself as I struggled to manage my emotions and transition to having this machine in our home.

I have always been a skilled compartmentalizer. I would go to a medical appointment like apheresis or dialysis, leave, and move on to my working-Liza-Mom-wife world. Never before had my medical life invaded my home space like an unwelcome intruder.

I cried a lot as I adjusted to home dialysis. When the first delivery came, a man carried more than thirty supply boxes upstairs and set them in the laundry room. I was inundated with medical supplies encased in cardboard—I felt besieged.

After some major purging and rearranging of the laundry's linen closet that is adjacent to our bedroom, I finally managed to store all the boxes out of sight. This was a small victory.

Then, Dirk ran the waste lines from the machine in the corner of our bedroom to our bathroom by duct taping them onto the carpet. So…of course…I cried some more.

Our beautiful, peaceful bedroom became a medical treatment room. The machine buzzed all night long and served as a constant reminder of the need to sustain my life by hooking up to this humming beast.

At the end of each run we were taught to initiate the rinse back. This procedure rinses the bloodlines and artificial kidney cartridge with saline so that the outstanding blood is returned to your body. It is an important step, and during our third home treatment, we had problems.

My Epogen shots had not kicked in yet so my hemoglobin was very low. I did not have much blood to spare. We started the rinse back process. The machine alarmed and then stalled—the rinse back was not happening.

"Dirk?!!!" I said with equal parts fear and hysteria, "why isn't it rinsing back?"

Dirk did not answer me. He was focused, and when Dirk is focused the world around him ceases to exist. Liza was sitting on the bed asking, "What's wrong Mom?"

"I need to get my blood back!" I said, as I remembered Mary telling me the blood needs to be returned in four minutes—or it will clot within the lines. I also imagined how low my hemoglobin would be if I lost this blood, and I feared a trip to the emergency room would be necessary.

Dirk stayed focused and called the emergency number to get help. A service answered, took the message, and told him the on-call technician would get back to us.

Time seemed to stand still and I was in a panic. Dirk was calm. Liza was empathetic. "It will be okay Mom, don't worry."

The phone call came and the technician talked Dirk through it— he cleared the alarm and hit some buttons and the machine began to pump again as my blood was returned.

The experience underscored for me that this home dialysis was a serious undertaking. Liza said, "Wow...I can't believe they let you two do this!"

CHAPTER FIFTY-SIX

My mom and dad were in Mexico at the time, and my mom called to check in. "How are things going?" she asked.

I couldn't even say a word before I started sobbing on the phone. "Not good Mom, it is so hard. I don't know if I can do it. I wish you were home."

"Ooooh—it will get easier. This is a new thing and a big transition. Don't worry; you will adjust to this just like you always do. I will be home soon, okay…hang in there." Her empathy was palpable through the phone connection.

As always, she was right. The time passed, and run after run, it started to become routine. The fear went away as we gained experience and proficiency. Within a short period of time Dirk was scheduled to go out of town and I was on my own.

I knew I needed to be able to do the procedure myself because it was hard to rely on Dirk's schedule, and dialyzing at night was not optimal.

When Dirk was out of town, it reminded me of how I felt when Dr. Brown retired—no matter how much support I had, this condition was all mine. There was no escape for me.

My mom came over and learned how to help me at the end of the run. She became my care partner and we set up regular times when she would be there. Like always, she was up for a riot and made me feel less alone in my medical world.

Home dialysis became a significant part time job. The five to six runs a week in combination with set up and take down, supply management, record keeping, SAK and PAK management, lab work, and separate monthly clinic and doctor visits were more than I realized. So I had to make adjustments to my work life and tend to the business of staying healthy and staying alive.

CHAPTER FIFTY-SEVEN

Once again I enjoyed lots of support from friends who continued to serve up a bottomless cup of compassion. Beth, Aunt Lucy, cousin Amy, Carrie, Suzanne, Amy, Jane, Colleen, and many more were willing to keep me company as I sat in my room and had my blood cleaned.

We had a record amount of snowfall that winter. Many times as I was dialyzing (tucked into my corner chair with a cozy down blanket) I felt grateful I did not have to travel in the snow to a dialysis clinic.

I had issues with low blood pressure and would frequently become lightheaded after dialysis or eating. If I felt faint, I would sit or lie down until my pressure came back. When I was grocery shopping, if I had a sudden drop, I would just bend over and pretend to shop the bottom aisles until I felt better.

I continued to have frequent bladder infections and was seeing Dr. Young at the University. She had me come in for urine and blood tests. I watched ten tubes of blood get sucked from my arm and headed back to my office.

I felt light headed as I pulled into the office parking lot. I called Jane at the front desk, and said I was pretty shaky after getting my blood drawn, so I wouldn't be coming in. "You probably didn't have much blood to lose. Go take a nap." Jane said in her typical upbeat and comforting manner.

Soon after I got a call from Dr. Young. "Your hemoglobin is 6.6, almost half of normal. How do you feel?"

"That probably explains why I thought I was going to die when I was on the treadmill yesterday." I replied.

"Stay off the treadmill, it could strain your heart to exercise with such a low hemoglobin. You need a blood transfusion."

I called my mom. "You want to have a riot?"

"Sure! Where to?"

"University, Friday morning. Blood transfusion. I will pick you up at 8:30."

"Looking forward to it!" she said with enthusiasm. Good ole Mom, after all these years she still was able to make a medical procedure seem like an exclusive social invitation.

After the uneventful blood transfusion, my mom and I stopped at a bookstore and the pharmacy to pick up a prescription. We waited for thirty minutes as the pharmacist tried to resolve an insurance issue.

As we waited, the cashier cheerfully juggled both the counter and drive-through customers. She peppered her conversations with a southern accent and overly friendly banter.

"How ya doing baby? What can I get for ya today? Sure thing honey, any questions for the pharmacist?"

My mom was counting the number of times she said "Baby" "Honey" and "Darling", as I chatted with a kind older woman who sat down next to us in one of the folding chairs lined up against the wall.

I noticed her fresh-from-the-salon white teased hair, as she asked me, "Can you help me read the expiration date on this coupon? It is so small." I gladly read the date for her. She thanked me and proceeded to offer a tidbit of information.

"You know these ginger snaps are on sale, and they are really very good." she said with a twinkle in her eye. She held up a box of cookies for us to see.

"Sometimes ginger snaps are just too thick." she explained. "But these are thin, and they are really delicious. I just love them."

"I like ginger—I will have to give those a try."

"Oh you really should." she said with great conviction, and seemed pleased. She then bid us goodbye and walked out of our lives. As she walked away I noticed her black leather Prada bag and classic plaid Burberry scarf.

I watched her leave and wondered aside from the mundane ginger snap conversation, what other stories could she tell us? What had she experienced? Where had she been in her life? What had her eyes seen?

I reflected on how everyday we experience brief moments with people that we will never know. They momentarily wash onto our shore and then return and vanish indistinguishably into the vast ocean that connects us all.

CHAPTER FIFTY-EIGHT

As my mom and I were driving home, Dirk called me on my cell phone.

"Hi—how's it going?"

"Good, got the blood, got a new book, and all is well. How are you?"

"Great. Work was fine. Lots of appointments. I also called the University today. I talked to Cathy Garvey and set up an appointment to be tested to be your kidney donor. It is set for March 17."

That was so like Dirk. He just jumps right to it. What do you say when unexpectedly, in the middle of a casual cell phone conversation, your husband says he has made preliminary arrangements to give you his kidney?

"Wow. Thanks Dude. That was a pretty big call."

"Yeah, I wanted to get going on that. Well great Jenn—I will see you tonight."

I hung up and turned to my mom and thought about how amazing it was that she gave me her kidney over seven years earlier. Spilling over with gratitude and awe for the people in my life I told her "Dirk talked to Cathy Garvey, he wants to get tested."

"Everyone needs a Dirk." she said. We both smiled and drove home.

That night I was reading my new book about a woman's medical journey with a breast cancer, and I was devouring it page by page.

I sat tucked in the corner of our striped family room sofa, as the fireplace warmed us with dancing flames. My feet shared the upholstered ottoman with Dirk's feet, as he sat in the red chair and answered emails.

It was a common night as we sat together, sharing space, sharing moments in time, sharing our evening routine, sharing our lives.

I felt deeply absorbed by the words of this woman and her experiences. I transported myself into her story and out of my own life.

I thought to myself, I can't *believe* what she's been through, and put the book down. Then it suddenly occurred to me—I have been through quite a lot myself, and I recounted the activities of the day. My mom (who had donated my third transplanted kidney to me) accompanied me to a blood transfusion, while my husband matter-of-factly offered to give me his kidney (for my fourth transplant). Well, just plowing through another extraordinary ordinary day…

That night as we crawled into bed, tired and ready to fall into the sleep that would bridge us to next day—I reached over and grabbed Dirk's hand.

"Good night."

"Good night." he said as he kissed my cheek. Our hands squeezed tighter. In the still and wordless silence that followed, there was much said.

CHAPTER FIFTY-NINE

Before the blood transfusion, Liza asked in earnest, "Mom, should I be worried about your health?"

I wondered how do I answer that? Yes? No? Maybe? Worried about the transfusion, or worried about health issues beyond that? I told her "My blood levels are very low so I am going to get some more. It should all be fine. Let's not worry."

And so it goes. Blood transfusions. Math homework. Sleepovers with friends. Bladder infections. Feed the dog. Snowboarding outings. Dinner dates with Dirk. Netflix movies. Business strategy discussions. Client meetings. Outings with my mom. Emails from friends. Skin spots biopsied. Jokes. Family dinners. Messy rooms. Clean rooms. Dog haircuts. Skin cancers removed. Trips to the Mall. Offers to receive a new kidney.

Regular everyday life punctuated with medical management.

"It's hard sometimes." Liza said another day as I drove her home from school. I told her we had to make one of our frequent stops at the pharmacy, so I assume this sparked her thought.

"What is?" I inquired.

"Well, the kidney stuff—I mean...don't take this the wrong way..." she said uncomfortably.

"It's okay Lize. What are you thinking about?"

"Well, I think you do a great job. I just hope...I just hope it

171

doesn't happen to me."

"Oh my gosh—no!" I exclaimed. "This is not going to happen to you. This condition is not genetic." I said with certainty. "It's okay for me," I continued, "but it would never be okay for you." I want the conviction of my words to banish her thought forever.

Relieved, she looks at me, as though I have wiped away her doubts. "I do think you have an amazing attitude Mom, you handle everything really well."

"Thanks Lize, I try. I guess through it all I have just developed a philosophy to make it the best I can. I believe that the best thing to do is live happy…damn it."

She laughed at my word slip and said, "I like it. If you ever write a book, that should be your title."

CHAPTER SIXTY

Steve and Merly's relationship solidified, they became engaged, and started to plan their wedding. It was set for July 3, 2010 in Cartegena, Colombia. I wasn't going to miss it for the world.

I talked to Dr. Davin and the staff at the Home Davita Dialysis center about dialysis in Cartagena. Admittedly, I was very reluctant to do this—I thought it would be very frightening to go to a dialysis unit in a country where I did not speak the language. Dirk thought it was out of the question.

I gathered names of nephrologists in the Cartagena area and the location of a nearby hospital. Armed with this contact information, I decided to go for the long weekend and skip two dialysis treatments.

Liza flew to Colombia the day ahead of Dirk and me, and traveled with Mom and Dad, Aunt Lucy, cousin Amy, and Amy's husband Jim. My Uncle John and his wife Marcy were there as well.

Dirk and I flew to Miami the next day, and then boarded a connecting flight to Cartagena. We arrived without a problem, and took a taxi to the quaint hotel where Steve had arranged for our visit.

Our first night was spent on a boat with food, drinks, and dancing. The next day we walked and shopped, and sweated from the intense heat. That evening we went to the wedding, which was held at an old mansion in the city.

The pastor passionately performed the ceremony in Spanish. A translator then repeated his words in English with a heavy accent. He talked about the sacred institution of marriage without tolerance for infidelity, prostitution, and murder. Different language. Different culture. Different message.

Two young singers performed a song. All the Colombians guests joined in, and the song started to swell. Before we knew it we were enveloped in a song that claimed the space. People were singing with their eyes closed, and swaying to the music that moved them. This beautiful song and the surrounding voices swallowed us.

After the ceremony, Steve said, "I am not quite sure...but I think I just joined a cult."

Bubbles were pumped in and floated around us when the ceremony was over, and we were led downstairs to the outdoor dining and dancing reception area.

A buffet of delicious food was set up and we enjoyed an amazing meal. The dessert was served prior to the dinner, which is a Colombian custom. I was obsessing about my fluid ounces and potassium intake.

High potassium was my biggest risk factor—I simply wanted to avoid heart irregularities that could lead to death. Other than that, hey... no big deal.

Late into the night, fireworks lit the corners of the dance floor. Costumed dancers swooped in with colorful masks during the Colombian celebration called Crazy Hour (Hora Loca). Did I mention the release of live butterflies? The atmosphere was highly charged with festivity and the spirit of celebration.

The next day we went to a home on the Caribbean to continue the party. We boarded a bus to take us to the house, and the air conditioning was not working. It was very hot and I started to overheat—sweat, sweat, and more sweat.

I was so thirsty when we arrived at this oceanfront home, and salivated over the coolers of cold beer. Although I don't usually drink beer, I grabbed one and drank it with relish. It was the best, most refreshing, satisfying cold beverage I have ever had in my life.

Then I felt guilty—I was on day three without dialysis. How much fluid had I consumed? Could I eat anything today or would I exceed a safe potassium level? I became worried and agitated. I had to let it go, and trust that it was going to be okay.

The next day we flew home and arrived very late that night. It was too late to dialyze and we needed to make a new SAK so I could dialyze in the morning.

Morning came; I dialyzed and sent my labs in. My levels were within an acceptable range and I did not take on a lot of fluid due to the extreme heat and sweat.

The fear of going to Colombia was behind us—I was able to see Steve and Merly get married and had a glorious time without health repercussions. It was the trip of a lifetime, and concluded with great relief.

CHAPTER SIXTY-ONE

Mom continued to sit with me as I dialyzed at home, and many people offered to relieve her of her kindness to offer their own. Aunt Lucy was always willing to come when my mom was out of town. She made the time go fast with her witty and entertaining conversation.

My cousin Amy would also visit with me as we shared stories about our daughters classes at Breck School, beauty tips, family updates, and the ins and outs of momhood.

Beth came to be with me once a week and she dove in, asking to learn how to operate the machine and help me initiate the rinse back process. She was a quick learner and it was such a comfort to have her there. We caught up on our families, kids, husbands, and overall status of coping and mental health.

My life was full of friends and rich with the love of my family.

One Saturday, Dirk and I drove to the charming eastern Minnesota city of Stillwater. We walked around this pretty town located on the St. Croix River, had dinner, and browsed through quaint shops and antique stores. We passed by a tiny place with a sign that said "Palm and Tarot Card Reader."

"Do you want to?" Dirk asked.

"Sure." So I sat down and bared my palm to the eccentric woman draped with scarves and jewelry. (She did appear to be right out of central casting for this role.) She said I had a long lifeline, and was a strong woman. She "saw" I was having struggles this year, but emphasized it would get better. She expected a significant improvement for me in 2011.

Why not? I decided to believe her, changed my password to kidney2011 for good measure, and envisioned the following would be the year of my fourth transplant.

Liza was empathetic and compassionate during my home dialysis treatments. She would pull a chair close and share my big down blanket. She planned television shows we could watch together to make the time go faster. Project Runway, Glee, Man versus Food, and various movies made the two hours endurable.

She had been studying Spanish since kindergarten, and in 9th grade she added French to her class list. I took French for a few years in junior high and high school, and always loved the language and culture.

Dirk remembered when we first met I said "Au Revoir" to Dawn as she left to go back inside the apartment. Although he claims he *briefly* thought I was French, Liza found my crude French laughable as she meticulously learned the basics of grammar and pronunciation.

"I would love to go to Paris someday." Liza fancied one night while I was dialyzing.

"It would be great to go to Paris, but I can't go while I am on dialysis." I explained. "We will go sometime." I said noncommittally.

Dialysis runs continued, Monday, Tuesday, Wednesday, Thursday, Friday, Sunday; and Liza would sit with me when she could. As she told me about her French classes, she continued to talk about Paris.

"Liza," I declared, "when I am off dialysis, we are going to go to Paris."

CHAPTER SIXTY-TWO

The Emily Program continued to grow, and there were now over 300 employees. Dirk decided to expand beyond Minnesota, and set his sights on Washington State. He discovered eating disorder treatment was limited in Seattle, and opened an outpatient clinic there to address the need.

Extraordinarily, I felt my life had come full circle—Seattle was back in my life in a totally new and different way. My current and past worlds fused harmoniously.

Dirk started to travel to Seattle once a month, and The Emily Program rented an apartment near Pike Place Market. I went along with Dirk one weekend, and timed my dialysis day off to coincide with the visit. On our short trip, we checked out the local dialysis units available for future visits.

I had flashbacks of talking to the social worker that told me about the peritoneal procedure that would cause a distended belly, and the unit that was populated by prison inmates. So much had happened since I sat in that office at the age of 23.

Now, I was in need of a fourth kidney and had donor offers from so many family and friends. Our niece Kirstin volunteered to be tested to see if she was a suitable candidate. I was blown away by her gesture. At the young age of 24, she demonstrated remarkable compassion and a caring nature.

"Kirstin, this is a huge offer. You should look into it and give it some serious thought." I explained.

"I have looked into it. You're family. I want to try." she said with calm assurance. Her preliminary blood work was sent to the University, and we learned that she was not a compatible match.

My sister-in-law Emily also told me she would like to see if she was a match. Once again, the caring spirit of people in our lives was tremendous and extremely touching.

I had a good feeling about Emily's compatibility. I thought she might be the one. She called me after her test results came back and tearfully told me she was not a match.

Dirk's mom had just celebrated her 80th birthday and wanted to be considered as well. She so much wanted to help us, and it was hard for her to accept that she was ruled out because of her age.

Deb, a friend and therapist at The Emily Program wanted to be tested to see if she could be my donor. I told Dirk I was reluctant because she had a young daughter and was going through a divorce—I thought it was too much to put on her plate.

She sent me an email expressing that she felt strongly about it. She wrote that although she was not yet into Internet dating, she felt like she had a worthwhile profile under consideration and was seeking my interest. "Won't you please consider me?" she asked. More remarkable benevolence. But once again, not a match.

My parents' friend Charlie also was tested, even though I hardly knew him. Beautiful kindness. Not a match. My cousin Amy was tested. Not a match. Amy's husband Jim was tested. Not a match.

My sister-in-law Ann called a coordinator at the University to discuss if she could be a donor for me. She had a history of kidney infections so she was ruled out.

An interior designer I had worked with on custom home projects also called the University and was interviewed. He was ruled out due to previous kidney stones.

There were so many others as well, and it kept surprising me. I continued to marvel at the outpouring of goodness that kept flowing towards me. Despite whatever negativity was on the news or headlined in the paper, my truth is that people possess an infinite well of compassion and it never seems to runs dry.

Yet, my three previous transplants and high antibody levels were causing me to strike out. The blood test that measures antibody levels is called the PRA test (panel reactive antibodies). It determines how easy or difficult it is to find a compatible match based on antibodies in the blood. Antibodies can become elevated from blood transfusions, previous transplants, and pregnancy. It was not looking good for me.

Liza wrote an essay for school that she titled *Locate the Rainbow*. It was touching to read her view on the medical situation that enveloped our home.

"Blindfolded, my mother can enter a rainstorm and locate the rainbow in seconds. She has obtained the ability to keep the positive in sight no matter how treacherous the storm. Whether she is wildly dancing to the Cure or accurately impersonating Cher, my mom is continuously blessed with a song in her heart and a beat in her soul. Her philosophy is to appreciate the small amazements in life and soon, the larger issues disappear. Through this small speed bump we call dialysis, she helped me find my rainbow."

I was so grateful to read that Liza was seeking the positive and was able to embrace such a mature perspective. She started to collect shot glasses for me so I could use them to make the most of my measured ounces. She presented me with shot glasses from Chicago, New York, Boston, Naples, Minneapolis, and Seattle.

CHAPTER SIXTY-THREE

I lost weight and our friends and family were concerned that I looked frail. My sunken cheeks and bony body did not broadcast good health. I tried to eat larger quantities of approved foods, but my weight kept dropping. I could feel my metabolism burning like a furnace as the stress of another kidney failure took its toll.

My hair also started to fall out. Slowly but surely, once again, my thick brunette hair became thinner and thinner. I pulled it back into a ponytail and hoped it would not become too noticeable.

I confided in my friend Jane and she gave me honest hair feedback. "Can you tell?" I would ask, as I would allow her to examine the carefully placed ponytail on the back of my head. "You're good— no one will know."

Jane had empathy and experience, as she had lost her hair during her successful breast cancer treatment years earlier. She made breast cancer treatment look like a breeze, as she confidently and cutely sported baseball hats to school while her hair grew back.

Jane's daughter Leah was Liza's friend, so I met Jane through our girls and Breck School. Some friends know you because you have a long history of growing up and plowing through years together. Some friends result from instant connection and mutual understanding. Jane was one of these.

181

Because she had gone through medical hell, she had an unspoken knowledge of my ordeal. She did not pity me, she just realized I needed a little extra boost at this time and was at the ready to provide it. Intuitively, she always offered before I could ask.

Jane would offer to take Liza to school and back so I could go to the doctor and fit in a dialysis run. She made a list of movies we could watch while I sat in my chair, and brought over her signature homemade chicken noodle soup to spare me time in the kitchen.

While on dialysis, Giada deLaurentis and The Barefoot Contessa were my constant companions. The Food Network was one of my go-to channels and I picked up quite a few recipes, techniques, and tricks of the trade.

"It's a bummer you're on dialysis Mom" Liza said. "But I must say it has really done a lot for our family meals."

Jane referred to Dirk as Jeffrey, the well-kept husband of The Barefoot Contessa that apparently loves his Friday night roasted chicken. The show often features his goofy smile as he walks into their aroma-filled kitchen with great anticipation.

He is typically greeted with strong cocktails and his favorite meal. Jane would call and ask, "What's on the menu tonight for Jeffrey?" and text me pictures of his adoring grin.

Her amusing texts came at the right time, and the simple power of her "thereness," defined for me, the essence of friendship. She confirmed that connection heals. And her restored health and thick, gorgeous, brunette hair reminded me that a tree looks different in the winter than the spring. Winter has its own beauty, and spring would come again.

CHAPTER SIXTY-FOUR

When I was a sophomore in college, I went on a family vacation over Christmas break to Austria. Mom, Dad, Steve and I came together from Minneapolis, New York, and Seattle to enjoy some time together.

One day on our vacation, my mom and I ventured out from Innsbruck, and drove in our rental car destined for a town named Worgl. We had heard Worgl was a wonderful place and set out to find it.

As we traveled on our route, we passed several small towns that beckoned us to stay and enjoy their unique charms. As we would start to pass through these towns, we would look at each other and ask, "Should we stop?"

"No, let's not" we would conclude. "Let's keep going until we get to Worgl." We were determined to reach our destination. When we finally arrived in Worgl, we looked at each other incredulously. It was not what we expected; yet we had built it up on our minds to be the ultimate destination.

We laughed as we realized we passed up so many charming experiences in our relentless pursuit of Worgl. It seemed an appropriate metaphor for enjoying life. As you set your course, don't pass by the unplanned joy along the way.

CHAPTER SIXTY-FIVE

When Dirk and I were first married, we went to Cape Cod so Dirk could attend a Psychology conference. One of his conference acquaintances had recommended a bed and breakfast.

We envisioned a charming inn where we could tuck in and experience the peacefulness of the Cape. When we arrived we realized it was an older couple's home and they were offering a small bedroom.

We walked through the front door into a messy kitchen, and found a note on the counter that said, "Make yourself at home, we'll be back!" The note and kitchen counter were both covered with an army of ants.

Dirk looked at me. I looked at Dirk. My eyes wide, I urgently said, "DO something!" He made a few calls and we stayed at a more suitable, quaint, lovely (ant-free) place.

My mom's frequent comment of admiration popped into my mind "Thank God for Dirk." He has always been my reliable, loving, "DO-something!" guy. When I have teetered on the verge of a breakdown due to life overload—Dirk always rises to the occasion in big and small ways.

One day my work was stressful, my labs were fluctuating, and my mental resolve was waning. Liza was young and brimming with high energy. I was low energy. Nothing seemed more appealing to me than sleep. Dirk was going out for a work-related evening event and he knew I was frayed.

Liza had an equally lively friend over, and their volume was high. I was working on a client presentation and was flustered about what to make for dinner.

Dirk appeared in the kitchen like a white knight set out to save the damsel in distress. "Here" he said as he handed me a slip of paper with a hand written phone number. "You don't need to make dinner. Call this number when you are ready. A medium pizza is approximately $15.00; I am giving you $20.00. Give the pizza guy the $20.00, which includes tip. I'll leave the money on the counter."

He carefully presented the plan as though my brittle state may have impaired my cognition for simple things. "Wow... Dirk, you've thought through all the details on this one." I was thankful.

"You relax tonight, take it easy." he encouraged. "Love ya, see ya." he said as he kissed me goodbye and off he went. What do you call a guy like that? Among many other things—most definitely, a keeper. I phoned the pizza place, sat back, and reveled in my good fortune of being braided into life with Dirk.

CHAPTER SIXTY-SIX

After Dirk was tested to be my donor, we quickly discovered I had antibodies against his blood sample too. Dirk felt great disappointment that he could not be my kidney donor.

Dirk never gives up easily, so he pursued information on a program called the Paired Exchange Program. These programs are essentially like a kidney exchange—two people who need a kidney transplant, swap willing donors.

If Dirk was found to be a compatible match to another person that needed a kidney, then I could in turn receive a compatible kidney from another donor.

So many people cannot move on to better health if they cannot find a suitable match. Pooling all the people who want to give someone a kidney with those that need a kidney greatly increases the number of possible matches. Paired exchange is a giant step forward for transplantation.

Dirk and I went to the University of Minnesota Medical Center and met Margaret. She thoroughly explained the program to us. Dirk would require several tests to determine if he was healthy enough to have surgery. Lab work, EKGs, ultrasounds, chest x-rays, kidney function imaging—similar tests to those my mom had eight years earlier.

After the team of doctors at the University Fairview evaluated all the tests, Dirk was deemed to be a suitable candidate for the Paired Exchange Program.

We were both extremely excited about the possibilities this program offered. It seemed such a creative solution to increase the likelihood of finding a match, and offered hope that I may actually be able to get a new kidney. Somehow. Someday.

The doctors determined it would be in my best interest to remove my last transplanted kidney and create more space for the new kidney. So Milly was removed on January 6, 2011. After a six-week recovery, I was finally eligible to go on the active paired exchange list.

Prior to the surgery I had an ultrasound to determine the location of the kidney to be removed. As the ultrasound technician was sliding the round wand and cold gel over my lower stomach, she started to make conversation.

I was tired of medical procedures and did not feel like making small talk about my many kidney transplants. She inquired about my surgeries and asked what was next for me. I was polite but not fully engaged.

After the procedure was done, she walked me back to the lobby where my mom was waiting. "I have had three kidney transplants too." she said to my surprise.

"Really?" I said amazed. "When did you have your last one?"

"Three years ago, and it is going well. I am keeping my fingers crossed that it will last for a long time."

We talked a bit more in the hall and I sincerely wished her well. She went back to her job and I went back to meet my mom.

I remembered when I was first diagnosed with kidney problems; I felt I had crossed an imaginary line. I longed to return to the "other" side—the side where healthy people with perfect lives walked and biked around the lakes—the side I could only see with sad eyes through the barrier of my car window.

My many experiences had enlightened my perspective since then. There was no line. There were no sides. My life had been significantly altered, but suffering was in no way unique to me. Inexplicable events happen to all of us.

In the beginning "Why me?" filled my mind, yet I realized it was such a useless thought. There are an estimated 20,000,000 people with chronic kidney disease, and each and every one of us could wonder "Why me?"

Why her? Why him? Why anyone?

Suffering. Resilience. Strength. Acceptance. Compassion. Our lives are full of both sorrow and joy, and we are all connected through the predictable unpredictability we share.

CHAPTER SIXTY-SEVEN

It had been almost a year since my girlfriends went to Cabo, and we were making plans for our next trip. Everyone would have preferred to go to Mexico again, but my dialysis situation removed this option. We decided on Palm Springs because it was sunny and outpatient clinic dialysis was readily available.

We had a great time just being together and lounging at our chic Frank-Sinatra-style rental home. The contemporary ranch had a groovy vibe with plenty of bedrooms, a well-stocked kitchen, gathering spaces, and an outdoor hot tub and pool. The hot tub was relaxing, but unfortunately the pool's heater was not working. The pool water was freezing.

I maintained my diet and fluid restrictions while enjoying the company of my best friends. My thirst was intense and I envied each ounce of water they swallowed. Late one night, as I craved fluids, I dove into the ice-cold pool to immerse myself in the water I longed to drink.

We discussed our next trip and decided if I had a new kidney we would plan on Cabo. As the idea was discussed, my friends faces lit up at the thought Cabo revisited. Considering my high antibody levels, I sadly thought the odds were slim that I would have a transplant by the following year.

Home dialysis had become routine and I did not want to

complain. I had a loving support system and a beautiful home to dialyze in. But I had to admit I was growing tired of the restrictions. I felt trapped and wanted to bust out of the situation.

I daydreamed of an alternate and completely different life. I told Dirk and Liza that in my next life, I was going to be a hearty farm mom with lots of kids and animals. They laughed and said it was difficult (well…maybe they said impossible) to imagine.

"Yeah, a squeamish, well-manicured farm mom with a house keeper. Will you farm organic produce from the grocery store?" Liza asked sarcastically. Okay, so I admit I have always been more of a luxury-spa-resort-kind-of-girl as opposed to a rough-it-in-the-woods-camper.

"Well, if I am going to imagine a different life, it might as well be a stretch." I mused. "Hmmmm—perhaps I could be the Jackie O of pioneer women?"

I vented my increasing dialysis frustrations in a journal.

I want to wake up and drink a cup of coffee that exceeds two ounces.

I want to wake up and have a big bowl of fresh fruit with loads of potassium and fill a large glass with water or juice. No shot glasses in sight.

I want a hot brimming bowl of soup without thinking about the sodium, the fluid, the potassium, and skip the phosphorus binder afterwards to remove the bone robbing phosphorus from my system.

I want to stop counting potassium grams, fluid ounces, dialysis supplies, SAK hours that remain, and hours to fit in the procedure that cleans my blood.

Summer came and we maintained our 4th of July tradition to spend five days at a resort in northern Minnesota called Maddens. We successfully transported the dialysis machine and enjoyed our vacation despite the daily dialysis treatments.

We went swimming, roasted marshmallows, and took Liza and her friend Sophie tubing on the lake. Dirk and I went golfing and enjoyed the summer weather. As I was wrestling with my golf bag to place it on the back of the cart, Dirk came over to assist me. He effortlessly loaded the clubs on the cart as he goaded, "How's it going there farm girl?"

CHAPTER SIXY-EIGHT

We returned from Maddens and fell back into our summer routine at home. I got a call from Mary, my transplant coordinator. She said I was due for a mammogram and PAP smear, and I should take care of it right away so my file was up to date. She explained that when a kidney becomes available, it happens quickly, so I should not wait to get these things done.

I immediately set up my appointments to knock these things off my list. Mary's insistence made me wonder if something was brewing that influenced her urgency.

Soon after, Mary called again and said there was a possible donor for me. She could not be sure it would work out, but she said there was someone who may be a match, and they were looking into the compatibility.

"It is a really good kidney." she said.

I was cautiously excited. "What if this is it?" I thought with a surge of emotion. I told my mom and friends…but I was guarded. I explained there might be a good match available, but I did not know yet. I asked people to think good thoughts.

Margaret called Dirk and told him that if this possibility would work for me, then he would have surgery as well to donate his kidney to another recipient.

So we waited to hear more news, and hoped and prayed and

visualized and did everything in our power to will it to be true.

Liza was attending a summer class at the Minnetonka Center for the Arts, and I dropped her off each morning. The morning of August 2, 2011, as Liza and I were headed to her class, an incoming call was displayed on my Bluetooth monitor. We both saw on the screen that it was the University.

"Answer it!" Liza said with excitement.

"Oh my God." I blurted as I hit the button to receive the call. I pulled off on a side street and said "Hello?" as my voice cracked with nerves.

It was Margaret. She said the donor was a good match and there were a couple additional tests to complete, but it was looking very positive. In addition, she said the donor would like to schedule surgery as soon as possible.

I was dumbfounded, happy, scared, teary, shocked, and excited— so many emotions were bombing my brain. Liza heard Margaret's words as they were being broadcast through the car speakers. She was dancing in her seat with a huge smile.

Margaret asked if I could have surgery on August 19th. "Of course!" I exclaimed. She said Dirk's surgery would be the same day.

Liza started texting her friends. I called Jane and she readily offered any help I may need including giving Liza rides to school, food, anything. Jane told our friend Colleen and Colleen called right away. She cried.

I called my mom. I emailed Carrie, Lisa, Amy, Suzanne, Liz and Rachael. I texted Beth. Cousin Amy called—she was delighted. Steve called, Aunt Lucy called, Uncle John called, I emailed our neighbors Sylvia and Jim, and they told neighbor Gary, he called. Franny's mom Lisa called. The word spread quickly to all our friends and family and I felt lifted and supported by the excitement everyone shared.

Margaret called again and said the date was changed to August 25 due to the coordination of operating room availability. I asked what she could tell me about my donor, and she said he was a twenty-five year old young man in North Dakota.

He was an altruistic donor, meaning that he did not sign up for the Paired Program to direct a kidney to someone he knew. He simply went into the Kidney Transplant unit at the North Dakota hospital and volunteered to donate his kidney.

"He has been thinking about it for quite awhile," Margaret said. I was incredulous. He is twenty-five, how long could he have been thinking about it!

As I drove in my car after talking to Margaret, I was overcome with an impossible-to-articulate-joy knowing that a total stranger in this world was willing to greatly improve my life.

Macy Gray was on the radio and "Beauty in the World" played throughout my car. The words elevated me in combination with the knowledge of my donor's generosity.

We were told Dirk's kidney was going to a man in North Dakota that was in his sixties and had been sick for some time. He had diabetes, and Dirk's generosity was going to offer him renewed life.

I had a great deal of compassion for this man. I imagined the moment he received the call that he had been waiting for—the call that would change his life.

I thought of his family and friends that in turn received calls and their excitement for his opportunity. I felt a special connection between all of us.

Dirk did not focus on his kidney's destination; he just focused on the fact that I was receiving a kidney and his donation made it possible.

Dirk and I were both concerned about going into surgery on the same day. We wanted to be sure one of us was home with Liza while the other was in the hospital. Margaret understood and arranged Dirk's surgery for one week after mine; he was scheduled for September 1.

CHAPTER SIXTY-NINE

I knew my home dialysis routine was going to be over soon and I was overjoyed. In anticipation, I listed simple things I looked forward to after my transplant—including big refreshing glasses of ice water and a consistent blood pressure (to eliminate the sudden and annoying feeling that I might pass out).

The countdown was on.

14 DAYS BEFORE TRANPLANT

Mary from the University called and said all the doctors were putting their heads together to determine the best course for my treatment. She said the hope and goal was that my focal sclerosis could be managed.

I was scared.

Amy, Rachael, Suzanne, Carrie, and Liz came over and spent the night for a slumber party. Dirk was at a conference in D.C. and Liza was in New York visiting her Aunt Ann, and cousins Tika and Satchel.

I wrote a letter to thank the man who was donating his kidney to me. I read it to my friends and Liz passed around tissues to dry the tears that sprung from a mix of happiness and fear and hope and love.

Amy told us her yoga instructor had a kidney transplant and her husband was her donor. Amy told her about me, and her teacher decided to dedicate all her classes on August 25th to my surgery. The positive energy of friends, family, and strangers encircled us.

We all staked out different rooms to sleep in, and Liz stayed in my room with me. She was startled by the constant hum of the machine that I had gotten used to. In the middle of the night the SAK failed and there was a loud alarm indicating a fluid leak.

BEEP, BEEP, BEEP. I tried to read the manual in the dark. The alarm was bad enough—I didn't want to add insult to injury by turning on the light too. I drained what I could and faced a large tub of dialysate to deal with in the morning. Liz helped me towel it up and said it was the worst sleep of her life.

13 DAYS BEFORE TRANSPLANT

I was worried about the surgery because I had a bladder infection, but I felt it was improving from an antibiotic Dr. Young had prescribed. My anxiety was bubbling to the surface so I called Dirk and told him I was saturated with worries and I wanted to share them.

"Me too" he said, "I am your guy."

My neighbor Missy called to offer any help I may need. Her husband Bobby crossed the street and rang our doorbell. When I answered the door he gave me a big, supportive hug.

8 DAYS BEFORE TRANSPLANT

After a short getaway to Grand View Lodge on Gull Lake in northern Minnesota, we returned home. Mom, Dad, Dirk, Liza and I had wanted to escape before the surgeries, and Liza brought her friend Powell.

We rented a large cabin with three bedrooms, a large family room with a pool table, and a decent sized kitchen. Dirk and I had the largest room because it provided space for the dialysis machine and supplies.

On our last morning I was lounging in the bed with the stiff tan velour blanket and flimsy low-thread-count sheets. I heard the balls clinking on the pool table in the family room. Dirk and Liza were playing their last morning round of pool.

I stared at the field stone fireplace in front of me and I listened to their laughter. I realized that when we packed up and left, this place and time would be gone. Vacations are fleeting packages of time carved out of our typical days. They are enjoyed, and then they are done.

Transplants are like that too—and so is life. We have a series of moments carved out of our days that must be enjoyed…because nothing stays the same through time. Time robs us of one existence, and offers another.

After we left this cabin, other people would come and permeate the space with their own vacation, their own fun, and their own spirit. It made me hopeful and attached to the world somehow, knowing that the places and things we love do not start and stop with us. Other people move through them and enjoy them, and we all unify somehow in these shared experiences.

Best to savor…

CHAPTER SEVENTY

I knew what I was looking forward to if my transplant was successful, but what if it failed? I found comfort in my simple list—joys and beliefs independent of a successful transplant.

1. I believe sleeping in on weekends is an amazing treat— especially in clean, crisp, luxurious sheets.

2. I believe that bad Kareoke singing in front of a select crowd is fun…and somewhat of an unappreciated art form (have you *heard* my Cher impression?)

3. I believe in the power of a good book to expand and transport me to a new, and exciting place, and life is best when you greet everyday as an opportunity to learn new things.

4. I believe in the seduction of a perfectly struck golf shot that gives you idealistic hope you could one day be a decent golfer.

5. I believe the feeling of unrivaled freedom from driving in a great car with a really great song (blasting) never gets old.

6.   I believe sunshine is a health tonic.

7.   I believe a new lip-gloss and sunglasses (plus the perfect outfit) are temporarily transformative.

8.   I believe in the power of color (and could play with paint chips indefinitely).

9.   I believe if fabrics were a drug I would be an incurable addict; when I am in a room full of gorgeous fabrics I want to inhale them.

10. I believe that clearing clutter from my house, car, and purse clears clutter from my mind and life.

11. I believe it is a worthy accomplishment to serve a knock out dinner and revel in the rave reviews.

12. I believe in hard work and the satisfaction of a job well done.

13. I believe being a mom is extremely gratifying (even though it can be torture) and my daughter is a unique gem that will shine in amazing and impressive ways.

14. I believe my husband is a remarkable man in more ways than I could have ever imagined.

15. I believe the constant presence and support built into a family is an amazing system—whoever devised the family structure was brilliant. In fact, genius.

16. I believe my dog Timmy is a furry ball of tail wagging love, fun, cuteness, and frustration all wrapped up into one black and white package.

17. I believe that the sounds, smell, and color of the ocean can dilute my troubles and rearrange my perspective.

18. I believe in the likability and goodness of most people—it is just buried deeper in some than others.

19. I believe the power of laughter is magical.

20. I believe in Karma and compassion. The way you treat grocery store clerks, waiters, valet parkers, and the drugstore cashier—in essence, the way you flow through the world—truly matters.

21. I believe small compassionate acts are very big. Share your space, allow people to merge into your lane, and give a friendly wave.

22. I believe abundance is a natural state. If you put goodness into the universe, it returns the favor.

23. I believe in unforgiving optimism and stubborn hopefulness.

CHAPTER SEVENTY-ONE

August 25, 2011

The day arrived, the day I was to receive my fourth kidney transplant. Dirk and I pulled in to Fairview University at 5:30 a.m. We were shown to a hospital room, I was given a gown, weighed, and my vitals were recorded. Then we waited.

I had undergone a series of plasmapheresis treatments within the past several days. Plasmapheresis is a blood treatment that works somewhat like dialysis. Two needles are inserted in an access such as a fistula, to remove and return blood to a machine. In this case the machine does not filter the blood for fluid and toxins; the machine separates and replaces plasma.

Antibodies that could possibly cause rejection are within blood plasma, as well as autoimmune factors, so the treatment was set up to benefit my upcoming kidney transplant.

Plasmapheresis is followed by an IVIG infusion, which replaces the good antibodies that are removed from the plasma exchange. At 9:00 a.m., an IVIG infusion was started and the day dragged slowly on.

Since I had a recent bladder infection, Dr. Young had a plan that I would receive IV antibiotics before surgery to reduce the risk of serious infection problems. Dirk and I still had vivid memories of my septic infection after Liza was born and we were determined to ensure it never happened again.

At 1:00 p.m., I entered the pre-op prep area and the anesthesiologist resident introduced himself. He looked like he was sixteen. His youthful appearance and timid personality did not inspire confidence.

I was nervous about the possibility of infection and wanted reassurance that I was going to receive the IV antibiotic that we had discussed with Dr. Young. He did not know anything about it.

They started to wheel me into the operating room. Liza and Dirk hugged me first, then Mom and Dad, and off I went. The OR was green, sterile, and artic cold. I asked the anesthesiologist again if I could get the IV antibiotics before they put me to sleep so I would know I had received them.

He seemed unsure. Then in a flash the main anesthesiologist swooped in, connected a syringe to my IV, and that was the last thing I remember. Out.

When I woke up, I was in a post-operative recovery room and it seemed chaotic. The nurse took my temperature and it was elevated. I was groggy, in some pain, and scared. Dirk and Liza came in and I saw tears in their eyes. I asked if everything went okay; they did not answer me.

I kept asking the nurse if I had been given the IV antibiotics and he did not know. I told him about Dr. Young and my previous episode of sepsis. I pleaded with him to call her. He said my blood pressure was very low and his top priority was ensuring I had enough fluid to profuse the kidney. He was working urgently on what he thought was the first course of action required, and I was filled with panic.

I felt so vulnerable. Dirk said he was going to call Dr. Young. The nurse was irritated. A doctor I did not know came in and said I had not received the antibiotics. Then another nurse came in and said I did—it was confusing and frightening as I wafted in and out from the anesthesia.

At 2:00 a.m. I was transferred up to ICU. Dirk and Liza came in and I was elated to see them. I thought they were asleep at home. They had never left. Dirk had called my mom and dad and said there were some complications and they should come back to the hospital. At 2:15 a.m. my parents walked into the ICU as well.

My ICU nurses were wonderful and I was stabilized with antibiotics by the following day. I received a constant infusion of IV fluids, anti-rejection medications, IV prednisone, plasmapheresis, and IVIG. I didn't move much, I didn't feel much, and I slept a lot.

Eventually I was moved to the transplant floor on 6-D. The uncertainty of infection was behind us and I was in a much better post-operative state.

Liza started 9th grade while I was in the hospital. We were sad that I was not there to see her off on her first day of high school, but excited about the reason why. It was the first year she was not required to wear a tartan plaid skirt and navy cotton shirt—so she texted me a fashion show of outfit possibilities for her first non-uniform week.

I started walking and continued to receive IV's throughout the day. After four days I was discharged and was able to go home.

CHAPTER SEVENTY-TWO

We were delighted the surgery was done and I was coming home. I still had to return early in the morning for continued plasmapheresis and IVIG treatments, but it was a huge difference to be home and see Liza after school, have dinner, and sleep soundly in my own bed.

My creatinine had dropped from 7.5 before the transplant to a very healthy 1.0. My stomach was distended and sore, my appetite was non-existent, but my kidney was working well.

September 1, 2011

One week had gone by without dialysis! I was delighted I could sustain my life without the machine as a result of this magical gift.

One surgery was down, one to go. Although the anxiety about my surgery was behind us, we now had to power through the experience of Dirk's surgery. I was filling up with worries and nervous energy.

It was different in comparison to years earlier when my mom donated her kidney. Our surgeries were within hours of each other, so we were both done at approximately the same time. I woke up, was immediately told she was doing well, and then fell asleep from heavy sedation. For Dirk's surgery, I was fully alert to clearly focus on fear.

Dirk and I did not sleep at all the night before, and we arranged for a cab to pick us up at 4:45 in the morning. Liza stayed at my mom and dad's house that night so my mom could take her to school in the morning.

When we arrived at the hospital everything happened quickly. Dirk put on a hospital gown and nurses came and took his vital signs. Anesthesiologists came in to talk, and an IV was started after two attempts.

The first IV effort created a bloody mess and Dirk looked uncomfortable as another IV placement was taking place. He had been very stoic and matter-of-fact about the surgery until this moment. His eyes clearly displayed vulnerability.

A nurse came in and asked Dirk if he was anxious. He looked at me, his lower lip quivered, and he nodded yes. I pushed the nurse out of my way and jumped on top of him. As we shed tears and hugged, I wanted to melt into him and take away all his fear.

At that moment I fully felt our intense connection. His look expressed all we had gone through, and that we were in this life together. Thick and thin, up and down, better and worse…and better again.

As they gave him a sedative his face looked peaceful. He was quickly out and they wheeled his bed off to the OR. I took comfort in knowing he was asleep and the surgery would soon be over.

Still sore and slow moving, I walked from the hospital through a skyway to the Apheresis unit. I checked in for my plasmapheresis appointment. For the next two hours I sat in a hospital bed while my blood plasma was separated and replaced with albumin to protect my transplant; meanwhile, Dirk's kidney was being removed so it could be driven to North Dakota to save a stranger. What a day.

Hours passed and Dirk's surgery was finished. His surgeon, Dr.

Pruitt called me on my cell phone and said it went very well. Dirk would be in recovery for two to three hours, and I could see him after that.

At 3:00 in the afternoon, he was wheeled into room 504 on floor 6-D. He looked rough. He had goop in his eyes that looked like Vaseline, his voice was raspy and weak, he was in obvious pain, and very emotional. All the same, his relief was palpable, and he said in a strained voice how glad he was that it was over.

"We did it Jenn."

CHAPTER SEVENTY-THREE

Dirk wanted to walk right away. The nurse loved his attitude. He vacillated from sleeping soundly to suddenly waking up to proclaim, "I want to walk." No sooner had he said it—he would immediately drift back into slumber.

On his second day he walked quite a bit. He was determined to go home as quickly as possible. He managed his pain with painkillers and could not yet eat, but he was drinking a lot of fluids to flush his one remaining kidney. (After kidney donation, the other kidney typically compensates so the donor can live a healthy, normal life with one kidney.)

I stayed until 3:00 p.m. that day, and then went home relieved to know he was doing so well. My mom dropped me off at the hospital and picked me up because I could not drive so soon after my surgery.

She asked if I wanted to go to her home, or have her come to my house. I said no thanks to both, I just wanted to plop on my couch and rest. Liza was at Franny's house for a sleepover so I knew it would be peaceful at home.

I cuddled up with Timmy and flipped on *The Ellen Show* as I tried to decompress. During some humorous bit, I unexpectedly started to cry as waves of emotion flooded me and I attempted to process all that had transpired.

On the morning of the third day after Dirk's surgery, he called and woke me up. "Good news Jenn, I am coming home today." Day three and he was coming home! We were so excited.

Later that afternoon he was discharged. My mom and I went to the hospital and picked him up, and she brought us home. Our hospital stays were complete and we set forth to recover together. We compared incisions, pain levels, stomach status, energy, exhaustion; and we shared immense relief. The hard part was over. Let the healing begin.

"I have new appreciation for all you have gone through." Dirk said one afternoon as we were both hobbling around the house. "Major surgery is not all it is cracked up to be."

It hurt to laugh, so his attempt at humor was painful as we both hugged our pillows to minimize the pressure on our incisions.

"Don't make me laugh."

"Don't make *me* laugh."

I went to a client meeting within twelve days of my surgery. My client knew about the surgeries and quipped, "Wow, your husband must *really* like you."

Dirk was back at work in a week and we went to an evening function at Liza's school that night. Kind friends surrounded us and they marveled that we were out and about. We were healing—in public, no less.

I continued to have frequent lab checks, plasmapheresis, and IVIG, but no dialysis. My mom often came with me to these post-transplant treatments. She was secretly delighted to be there when she discovered the twenty-four hour Law and Order channel. She sat with me and indulged in a marathon of crime solving television.

Dr. Issa was steadfast in his commitment to my post-transplant management. He felt it best if I started with three plasmapheresis and IVIG treatments a week. Then it was reduced—twice a week, once a week, once every other week, and once a month—until my first year was behind me.

During this time, my hair was becoming full again, my slight curves were restored, my kidney was working, and I regained strength and energy.

I sailed through the treatments by focusing on the benefits—the time to read a good book, more Food Network, HGTV, and the unbeatable comfort of heated blankets. One of the nurses and I had the brilliant idea of rebranding plasmapheresis as a spa treatment; a two hour filtration of your plasma marketed as a refreshing detox service. We imagined making millions...

I cherished the camaraderie with the nurses that were dedicated to my care. They were far from indifferent staff doing a job—the nurses and technicians were people just like me. People with ups and downs in their lives, people who cared and shared.

I learned of weddings, divorces, vacations, struggles to make ends meet, college applications, the difficulties of Internet dating, the joys and pains of raising an autistic child, new draperies, alcohol abuse, kid's high GPAs, Halloween costumes, and honeymoons. We shared time and the stuff of life.

Our connections reminded me again of how we are all linked through living, and by sharing our stories, a thread that runs through us is tightened just a little bit more. I propelled easily through my days with immeasurable gratitude.

CHAPTER SEVENTY-FOUR

It is not encouraged for donors and recipients to meet each other, but Margaret told me I could write a letter to my donor and the transplant clinic would forward it on.

Dear Donor,

I have never met you, but of this I am sure—you are a hero. I am overflowing with gratitude because the world for my family and me is changed dramatically because of your generous spirit.

Thanks to you I have become free from what my daughter calls the metal beast. Although we appreciated the machine that kept me alive, it felt like an intruder that repeatedly robbed us of our regular life.

Thank you for all the good health and time you are giving to my family and me. The value of your gift is impossible to measure. The gift of time, the gift of travel, the gift of unrestricted fluids, the gift of enjoying food, the gift of a regular blood pressure, the gift of energy, the gift of eliminating the wear and tear on my body and soul from five to six dialysis treatments a week...the gift of easy laughter and happy days.

I so wish I could adequately convey our gratitude—but in several attempts I realize words cannot express my emotion and thankfulness. You are a remarkable person and the world will forever be a better, brighter place because of you.

All the best to you and your family,
Forever Grateful,

Your Recipient

Liza also wrote a letter right before my surgery.

Dear Somebody,

As I write this, you are nine hours away from forever changing my life. For out of the kindness of your heart, you have subjected yourself to enduring the removal of your organ, the immediate pain that will follow and worst of all— hospital food. You have risked your life, simply to save a woman you have never even met.

Everyone loves my mom. Through almost two years of dialysis, surgeries and medication, her life has never come close to earning the title of a "pity party." She looks at life with a certainty that she was meant to enjoy every moment. And she does. But my mom does not deserve kidney failure. I doubt anyone deserves such a horror. However, she handles it with more grace and composure than most people can maintain after receiving a parking ticket.

Words cannot express how much you mean to me. This is my ninth draft of this letter and I am still unsatisfied. How can I convey to you, through words, that what you're doing is probably the kindest thing anyone has ever done for anyone in the history of everything…I can assure you that with your kidney, my mom will:

a.   enjoy every smoothie, shake and juice she was previously discouraged out of drinking.
b.   run/walk/jump everywhere she previously couldn't because of her low blood pressure.
c.   dance for her daughter
d.   live life like she once couldn't.

Once you have completed your never-ending stay at the hospital, you may resume your life, as if you still possess two kidneys. But by the time you have left the hospital, our lives will be changed forever. Thank you.

The Luckiest Fourteen Year Old in the World.
(Your Recipient's Daughter)

And of course, I wrote a little thank you note to Dirk.

Dearest Dirk,

I thank you for championing this health challenge with your characteristic problem solving determination and unconditional support. Thank you for the complete way you love me. Thank you for fully demonstrating that we are in this life together.

I look forward to all the good health we will share with this kidney. Let's appreciate every good day it offers. And I hope one day when we are a very, very old couple, we will look back on our years of good life, call up a foggy memory, and say "remember when we both had surgery in 2011?"

Liza says I can locate the rainbow in the middle of the storm. She may be right because it is very clear to me. As I look for all the rainbows in my life—the most vivid and beautiful rainbow I see is you.

I love you Dirk.

Jenn

CHAPTER SEVENTY-FIVE

After my second transplant, I started to be concerned about the appearance of the fistula in my arm. It was a large bulging vein and it made me feel self-conscious. I asked my Doctor if something could be done about it, and he recommended I talk to the surgeon that created the fistula years ago.

I remembered his name because the surgery had been so upsetting. At the appointment, I showed him my fistula, explained that I had been transplanted, and asked if I could get the prominent bulge reduced.

He explained that it would not look significantly better if he reduced blood flow within the vein, and the fistula was a useful insurance policy in the event I would need it again for dialysis. He reinforced that transplants are a vacation from dialysis.

I thanked him for his opinion, and reminded him he put the fistula in many years ago. I did not remind him of his outburst when he thought he punctured my lung. I shuttered for a minute when the traumatic scene flashed through my mind.

Then a look of remembrance registered on his face. "Oh I remember you!" he exclaimed. "I was so worried about you. You were such a young girl and I didn't know what would become of you. You had such fragile veins and seemed so sick. Look at you now!" He seemed genuinely delighted.

"I know!" I agreed. "I have a good life."

"Are you married?"

"Yes!"

"Do you have any children?"

"Yes! We have a daughter."

To my amusement, he asked as if it was the cherry on top, "Do you have a dog?"

"Yes!" and we both laughed.

If only he would have asked if I had a house, he would have been right in step with my engagement acceptance check list.

"I am really glad to see you doing so well—I don't think I would have predicted it all those years ago. I am so glad you came to see me. You have made my day."

I left his office feeling elated. He truly was happy for me, and it erased the previous experience from my mind. It was very clear to him, and to me—I was really was so much more than a "goddamn nephrotic!"

CHAPTER SEVENTY-SIX

Winter approached and our annual girlfriend trip was planned. A lot had happened in the year since we were in Palm Springs. I was thrilled to purchase my ticket to celebrate good health with friends in Cabo.

February 2012

We stayed in a beautiful home, lounged by the pool, and caught up on our lives. Rachael and Suzanne created a colorful buffet of sliced oranges, mango, pineapple, grapes, tomato focaccia, and fluffy scrambled eggs.

Liz also hired chefs to cook lovely dinners for us. We indulged on fresh salads, lobster and steak, and fresh strawberry parfaits. We relaxed by the pool with midday cocktails, and enjoyed intense conversations on the rocky shoreline of the Sea of Cortez.

It was, as always, an amazing stretch of relaxation and connection. And...I did not measure one ounce of fluid or count one milligram of potassium.

We toasted to my new kidney and renewed health status before one of our chef prepared meals. The first course was a shrimp appetizer. As I was enjoying the delightful tastes and loving friendships, I suddenly felt a lump as I swallowed. I reached for my water to wash down a little shrimp that I apparently did not chew very well.

I tried to swallow but the lodged shrimp prevented the water from going down. Panic overcame me as I realized I was choking on a shrimp. I got up and fled to the bathroom to see if I could force it up with a cough.

Of course, Carrie, Amy, Suzanne, Liz and Rachael were startled. They ran back to see what was happening and I looked at Rachael and eked out, "Choking."

She took immediate action and quickly heimliched me. The shrimp dislodged and I spit it in the sink. Crisis averted; we returned to our meal. We sat there for a moment, stunned from what just happened. Relief pooled with fragile emotions and Amy and Rachael started to cry.

"Jeez Jenny" Carrie said afterwards. "I think it is enough for us to worry about your four transplants, can you do us a favor and not choke on your food."

Since we share so much history, being together is like comfort food for our souls. We care about each other, and we carry each other.

Our lives have woven together through kindergarten teachers, trick or treating, royal blue polyester zip-up short suits for gym class (really awful), junior high crushes, tennis teams, inspirational teachers, horrible teachers, football games, diets, drinking, college, boyfriends, lovers, losers, marriages, divorce, carbohydrates, the environment, dirty martinis, yoga, Pilates, gluten, Ambien, SPF and skin care.

Our conversations have evolved dramatically through the years, as well as our tolerance to late nights and hangovers. Now that we are firmly planted in adulthood, we press on with more depth, more wisdom, more love, and more loss.

We could not grasp or know when we were in elementary school all that was ahead. We could not possibly imagine the wonder of our children. We could not possibly fathom the concept of planning funerals for some of our mothers, fathers, and unspeakably, a sibling and friend.

Nothing prepared us for the initial devastation, and subsequent premature miracle of a beautiful girl named Lola. We did not anticipate in-vitro disappointments followed by the adoption glory of wonderful Emma. Nor marriage troubles, marriage triumphs, financial ups and downs, the devastation of Alzheimer's, kidney transplants, and the joys of being alive.

But we do know now...that we can cry, we can laugh hysterically, cry some more, and laugh again, and value that we are one lucky tribe...as we continue to muddle through the thick and thin of our lives together.

CHAPTER SEVENTY-SEVEN

June 2012

In June after Liza completed 9th grade and her first year of French classes, we boarded a non-stop Delta flight bound for Paris. The flight was fairly uneventful with the exception of an inconsolable baby boy sitting in front of us with his parents.

He cried for an hour straight and his mother seemed very flustered. To our horror, she eventually attempted to hush his loud cries by placing a thick blanket over his head. Her husband took him from her and removed the blanket.

We arrived in Paris early in the morning, and were greeted by Patrick, who chauffeured us to our apartment in sluggish morning traffic. One and a half hours later we got there and were greeted by Justine. She let us into the apartment and acquainted us with the surroundings.

She showed us to our third floor apartment and led us up a narrow stairway with red walls and red carpet. Dirk placed our luggage in the tiny elevator, as per Justine's recommendation, so we would not need to carry them up the three flights.

When we tried to retrieve our luggage from the elevator, we discovered the bags had shifted forward during the climb and lodged the elevator door shut. It would not open. No luggage.

Although we were exhausted with jet lag, we ventured out, as Justine promised to get a technician in to free our luggage. We had a lovely French breakfast with strong coffee, and warm baguettes dripping with jam.

Upon returning after some shopping, we discovered our key would not fit in the lock and open the door. No access to luggage. No access to the apartment.

Dirk left many stern messages with Justine—he went full bore American on her and clearly stated our expectations for immediate action and customer service. To add to the intensity, I had anti-rejection medications in my bag and needed to take them on schedule.

Later than sooner, a technician came and freed our luggage. Then the key hiccup was remedied so we could open our door.

Dirk and I observed we had a knack for adventurous starts when we travel to France. Now things were looking up, and we were ready for the rest of the trip to unfold.

We spent ten glorious days in Paris, and fully embraced the wonder of the city, the wonder of our good fate, and the wonder of it all.

The evening of Bastille Day, we walked to the Eiffel Tower and saw an enormous firework display exploding behind the impressive Paris structure.

As the fireworks lit up the sky, American disco songs blasted all around us. The colorful lights, the outline of the Eiffel Tower, and the instantly recognizable 1980's "Funkytown" collided into a spectacular evening.

Dirk and I had come a long way since we were last in Paris on our honeymoon eighteen years earlier. As we stood together with our fifteen-year-old daughter at the base of the iconic iron monument…celebration was definitely in the air.

CHAPTER SEVENTY-EIGHT

August 2012

I went to see Dr. Issa for my one year follow up appointment. I sat in the full waiting room with several other patients. Some appeared very ill, some seemed just like me. I looked up and saw Cathy Garvey walking by.

"Hey what are you doing here?" she said in her upbeat style.

"Just a check up…feeling good." I beamed.

"That's what I like to hear. Make it an in and out visit."

"That's my plan." We both grinned and said goodbye.

I was called back and sat in a small room. Dr. Issa came in and we greeted each other with a big smile. He asked how I was doing, reviewed my medications, and agreed that I had a very good first year.

"Let's make this the first of many more to come," he said with warm optimism.

Then he asked me all about our trip to Paris and we shared a mutual appreciation for the city. It was thoughtful he recognized our trip was significant, because just over one year ago it would not have been possible.

We came up with a plan to manage my ongoing lab appointments and monitor my proteinuria. We shared positive impressions about my progress, set my next appointment, and said goodbye.

I walked out of the small exam room feeling jubilant about how well this year had gone. I had friendly banter with the woman at the appointment desk, picked up a jug for my next urine collection, and was on my way.

As I walked out, I passed a young girl walking in. She had a bouncy blonde ponytail and wore shorts and a t-shirt. Although she looked tan and athletic, I could sense a familiar uncertainty in her face. Her mother, who appeared concerned and ready to take charge, accompanied her.

I saw my younger self in her, and wondered about her clinic visit. Was she going to need a biopsy? Was she going to find out she had a kidney disease? Was dialysis or a transplant in her future? She was so young and appeared to have her whole life ahead of her. I sent her positive thoughts and hoped she would be okay.

I briefly flashed back through my twenty-plus year journey, and realized no matter what her medical status, she would have many of her own successes as well. I wanted to turn back and assure her "Don't worry, it will be okay. If you get knocked down by life's fist, you will get back up."

No matter what she encounters, she can deal with it and find a good life with love and joy along the way. She should proudly display photographs of her family and friends and appreciate the miracles in every day. Endure the lows. Celebrate the highs.

And—despite it all—live happy.

(...damn it)

Jennifer Cramer-Miller

Immeasurable Gratitude:

To the all the amazing transplant doctors, surgeons, providers, coordinators, nurses, lab technicians, plus Apheresis nurses, SIPC nurses, residents, interns, cooks, valet parkers, greeters—all the dedicated staff and volunteers—at the University of Minnesota Medical Center Fairview. This book and my life would not be possible without you.

To Dr. Issa—thanks for putting your full brain into my case and sharing my determination to make the best of what can be.

To all the hard working nurses and technicians at Davita—you make a tough situation better by doing what you do with care and a smile.

To Dr. Davin—you are one-of-a-kind and I am very grateful for your expertise, random bouts of French (Bonjour!) and most charming nature. Plus all the wonderful nurses at your office are amazing, caring people.

To the doctors and nurses at the Neonatal Intensive Care Unit at Hennepin County Medical Center—your special skills are a gift to all of us that trust our fragile and precious preemies to your care.

To Dr. Brown—thanks for good care, and showing me that doctors can really care about their patients.

To my family—Dirk, Mom, Dad, Steve, Merly, all the McInnis', Millers, McNultys, Cramers—what can I say? Words can't articulate my appreciation and love.

To my remarkable friends—you know who you are and I love you.

To Liza—keep shining your unique light and you will illuminate the world.

ABOUT THE AUTHOR

Jennifer Cramer-Miller is a daughter, sister, wife, and mom. She has been immersed in the custom home industry for more than twenty years, devours all things interior design, and now masquerades as an author.

In her spare time she enjoys healthy cooking, ample laughter with friends over coffee or cocktails, and valiant attempts to avoid humiliation on the golf course with her husband.

Jennifer lives with her daughter, husband (and Timmy, a fluffy black and white Tibetan Terrier) in a western Minneapolis suburb.

AUTHOR'S NOTE

Ellen DeGeneres and Madonna randomly inspired the completion of this book. I realize that sounds far-fetched...but one day on *The Ellen Show*, Madonna explained that she encouraged Ellen to come out with her personal story. She made it clear that if Ellen didn't tell it—no one else ever could. We all have our own unique stories.

That struck me, as I realized I was the only person in the world that could tell this story. Empowered, I sat down at my computer, wrote and wrote some more, and eventually—this book was born.

Additional copies of Live Happy (...damn it) are available by simply searching the title at Amazon.com.

Live Happy (...damn it)

References:

1. Buechner, Frederick, The Book of Bebb, 2001 Paperback Edition, Harper Collins Publishers, Source ISBN 978-0-06-251769-2, Source Chapter: Open Heart, Chapter 17, Source Page Range: Page 251
2. The Brady Bunch, ABC, KSTP. 1969-1974. Television.
3. Ross, Herbert, dir. Steel Magnolias. Tri-Star Pictures, 1989. Film.
4. Campbell, Joseph, A Joseph Campbell Companion, Reflections on the Art of Living, edited by Diane Osbon. Harper Collins Publishers, New York, NY, 1991.
5. Reiner, Rob, dir. When Harry Met Sally. Ephron, Nora screenplay. Columbia Pictures, 1989. Film.
6. Siegel, Bernie, M.D.. Love, Medicine, and Miracles: Lessons Learned about Self-Healing from a Surgeon's Experience with Exceptional Patients. Quill, January 1986, Print.
7. Simon, Carly. "Coming Around Again." Coming Around Again. Arista Contemporary, 1987. Album.
8. Marley, Bob. "Three Little Birds." Exodus. Chris Blackwell. 1977. Album
9. Dufty, William. "Sugar Blues." Chilton, Book Company 1st Edition (1975), Print.
10. Carper, Jean. The Food Pharmacy: Dramatic New Evidence That Food is Your Best Medicine, Bantam, 1989, Print.
11. Carnegie, Dale. How to Win Friends & Influence People. Pocket Books, 1988, Print.
12. Siegel, Don, dir. Dirty Harry. Milius, John. Riesner, Dean. Fink, Harry Julian. Fink, R.M. Screenplay. Warner Bros., 1971. Film.
13. Scorsese, Martin, dir. Taxi Driver. Schrader, Paul. Screenplay. Columbia Pictures, 1976. Film.
14. Bach, Johann Sebastian. "Jesu, Joy of Man's Desiring." 10th and last movement of the Cantata Herz und Mund und Tat und Leben BWV 147. 1716. 1723. Piano.
15. Purcell, Henry. Trumpet Tune. 1600's.
16. Morrison, Van. "Brown Eyed Girl." Blowin' Your Mind! Bang Records. 1967. Album.
17. Thiele, Bob. Weiss, George David. "What A Wonderful World." Recorded by Armstrong, Louis. What A Wonderful World. Single. ABC,

HMV. 1967. Album.

18.   Hathaway, Sandee; Eisenberg, Arlene; Murkoff, Heidi; Mazel, Sharon. What to Expect When You Are Expecting. Workman Publishing Company, 1984. Print.

19.   Murkoff, Arlene; Hathaway, Heidi; Eisenberg, Sandee, What to Eat When You Are Expecting. Workman Publishing Company, 1994. Print.

20.   Ferry, Bryan. "More Than This." Avalon. Polydor/E.G./Atco. 1982. Album.

21.   Miller, Liza. A Mother's Love. Essay.

22.   Curly Girl Design, SEND LOVE. 'Even If She Weren't My Mom' artwork and words ©2008 Leigh Standly publishing ©Curly Girl Design Inc./Leigh Standley www.curlygirldesign.com

23.   Grogan, John. Marley & Me: Life and Love with the World's Worst Dog, William Morrow, 1 edition (October 18, 2005), Print.

24.   Miller, Liza. Zoe and Me. 3rd grade essay.

25.   Miller, Liza. Locate the Rainbow. 8th grade essay.

26. The Barefoot Contessa, The Food Network, Channel 231, 2011, Television.

27.   Gray, Macy. Cross, Kannon. Lopez, Joshua. Reichart, George. "Beauty in the World." The Sellout. Island, Concord. 2010. Album.

28.   Miller, Liza. Letter to Kidney Donor. September, 2011.

Sources:

1.   United Network for Organ Sharing (UNOS) www.unos.org

2.   Living Kidney Donors Network, www.LKDN.org Matching Recipients and Donors

3.   University of Minnesota Medical Center Fairview uofmmedicalcenter.org/specialties/kidney transplant

4.   National Kidney and Urologic Diseases Information Clearinghouse (NKUDIC). A service of National Institutes of Disease and Digestive and Kidney Diseases (NIDDK) National Institutes of Health (NIH), Kidney Disease Statistics for the United States.

5.   www.Davita.com, Davita: Kidney Disease and Dialysis Information

Made in the USA
San Bernardino, CA
14 January 2014